Elementary Nuclear Theory

This course was given at the Research Laboratory of the General Electric Company at Schenectady, New York. The notes were taken by

MELVIN LAX

CONRAD LONGMIRE

ARTHUR S. WIGHTMAN

Elementary Nuclear Theory

A SHORT COURSE ON SELECTED TOPICS

By H. A. Bethe

Professor of Physics at Cornell University

1947

JOHN WILEY & SONS, INC., NEW YORK

CHAPMAN & HALL, LIMITED, LONDON

(Physics)

PREFACE

This book is not meant to be a textbook of the theory of atomic nuclei. It is merely a selection of certain topics in the theory, and even these topics are treated in only an elementary way. Until a more complete textbook is written, the reader who wishes to obtain a thorough knowledge of nuclear theory will have to consult the original literature, or for certain topics the articles of the present author in *Reviews of Modern Physics* (Vol. 8, p. 83, 1936; Vol. 9, pp. 69 and 245, 1937).

The emphasis in this book is placed on the problem of *nuclear forces*. This problem is the central problem of nuclear physics. The problem is treated entirely from the empirical point of view, and I have made an effort to present the evidence available on nuclear forces from the behavior of the simplest nuclear systems. Purely theoretical considerations about nuclear forces, particularly the meson theory of these forces, are treated with the greatest brevity, because they are not yet in a form in which they would permit useful predictions.

As a second field of nuclear physics which is sufficiently well developed and fundamental, I have chosen the theory of beta disintegration.

The theory of the compound nucleus and its consequences for the prediction of the probabilities of nuclear reactions I have treated only very briefly. The reason for this was partly a matter of time: the lecture course on which these chapters are based contained only twenty lectures, and it seemed more profitable to treat part of the theory thoroughly than to treat all of it superficially. Partly, however, the brevity of treatment of the more complicated nuclei was purposeful; in the last ten years the workers in this field have shown an inclination to devote a large proportion of their effort to the study of the complicated nuclei, and the danger exists that the right perspective may be forgotten. The wartime research in the atomic energy project tended further to emphasize the usefulness of the predictions from the theory of the compound nucleus. To correct this tendency, it seemed even more important to put special emphasis on the fundamental theory of nuclear forces and off the theory of the complicated nuclei.

The theory of the fission process has been left out entirely for the same reason: this process is, after all, only a very special phenomenon in nuclear physics.

The theory of alpha radioactivity could be left out with a good conscience because it is given in many elementary textbooks on wave mechanics. With some regrets I also had to leave out the theory of nuclear systems containing from 3 to 60 nuclear particles, especially the successful calculations of binding energies on the basis of group theory by Wigner.

H. A. BETHE

CORNELL UNIVERSITY
  July, 1947

CONTENTS

A. DESCRIPTIVE THEORY OF NUCLEI

I. BASIC FACTS ABOUT NUCLEI

Each atomic nucleus has a charge Ze, a mass M, and a mass number A. Ze is an integral multiple of the charge e of the proton. M is very close to an integral multiple of the proton mass. The integer A which gives the multiple closest to M is the mass number.

The nuclear charge Z determines all the chemical properties associated with an element. It has values from $Z = 0$ (neutron) to $Z = 96$ (curium) for observed nuclei. Some of these do not occur in nature: $Z = 0$, 43, 61, 85, 87 (87 occurs in very small abundance as a member of a branch of the radioactive family of Ac), 93, 94, 95, 96.

The mass number A ranges from $A = 1$ (proton or neutron) to $A = 242$ (curium). Nearly every mass number in this range is found in nature. The notable exceptions $A = 5$ and $A = 8$ have good reasons for not being stable long enough to be observed even in the laboratory. The mass numbers of form $4n + 1$ beyond 209 (Bi) are not found in nature but many of them have been produced in the laboratory. These nuclei belong to a radioactive series which does not contain any long-lived members and, therefore, could not have survived on earth.

Isotopes. Nuclei of the same Z but different A are called isotopes. On the average there are about three stable isotopes for each Z. To distinguish isotopes A is usually written as a right superscript and for convenience Z is sometimes written as a left superscript. To illustrate: Si^{28}, Si^{29}, and Si^{30} are the stable isotopes of Si. In addition to the stable isotopes, most elements also possess radioactive isotopes, e.g., Si has the known isotopes Si^{27} and Si^{31}. Of these, Si^{27} is β^+ radioactive (having too little mass for its charge) and decays with a half-life of 4 seconds to Al^{27} and a positron

$$Si^{27} = \beta^+ + Al^{27}$$

Si^{31} (having too little charge for its mass) decays with a half-life of 170 minutes to P^{31} and an electron

$$Si^{31} = \beta^- + P^{31}$$

1

Isobars. For a given A, there may well be several possible values of Z (isobars). There are many instances of stable isobaric pairs, e.g., $^{22}\text{Ti}^{50}\ ^{24}\text{Cr}^{50}$, or $^{44}\text{Ru}^{104}\ ^{46}\text{Pd}^{104}$, and some stable isobaric triples, e.g., $^{40}\text{Zr}^{96}\ ^{42}\text{Mo}^{96}\ ^{44}\text{Ru}^{96}$, as well as numerous radioactive isobars.

Regularities. There are several striking regularities in a table of the stable nuclei. Nuclei of even Z are much more numerous than those of odd Z. Nuclei of even A are more numerous than those of odd A. Nearly all nuclei with even A have even Z; the exceptions are $^{1}\text{H}^{2}$, $^{3}\text{Li}^{6}$, $^{5}\text{B}^{10}$, and $^{7}\text{N}^{14}$. (There are also $^{19}\text{K}^{40}$ and $^{71}\text{Lu}^{176}$ but these are not properly stable, being β-radioactive with very long lifetimes.) The fact that nuclei with odd Z cannot have even A with the listed exceptions is what makes stable nuclei with even Z more numerous than those with odd Z, for a nucleus with even Z may have A either odd or even. Table 1 illustrates

TABLE 1

SAMPLE OF ISOTOPE STATISTICS

Z	Number of Stable Isotopes	Number with Odd A	Number with Even A
48	8	2	6
49	2	2	0
50	10	3	7
51	2	2	0

all three rules. For odd A, there is apparently no preference between even Z and odd Z.

Energy. In considerations involving the energy of nuclei the mass M is important. According to Einstein's relation, the energy equivalent of a change in mass ΔM is

$$\Delta E = \Delta M c^2$$

Such changes in mass occur when protons and neutrons are changed from one configuration to another in which they are bound more or less strongly. There is no evidence at present for the total annihilation of heavy particles (protons or neutrons). Such a thing might happen if an "antiproton" ($Z = -1$, $A = +1$) met a proton ($Z = +1$, $A = +1$) but the antiproton has not as yet been observed. On the other hand, the total annihilation of electrons and positrons with the emission of two light quanta does occur.

Modern mass spectrographic techniques permit the determination of M to better than one part in 10^5 (an improvement by another order of magnitude would just make possible the deter-

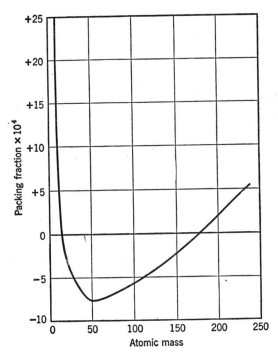

FIG. 1.   Packing fractions of atomic nuclei.

mination of the decrease in the atomic weight of a heavy atom due to the binding of the electrons in the field of the nucleus). From such data the binding energies of nuclei can be calculated. For example, using the atomic weight scale based on O^{16}

$$M(O^{16}) = 16.00000$$

there results (using the masses given in the Appendix) $M(^1H^1)$ = 1.00812, $M(n)$ = 1.00893. Supposing that the O^{16} nucleus is made up of 8 protons and 8 neutrons, the binding energy is

$8M(\text{H}^1) + 8M(n) - 16.00000 = 0.13640$ mass unit. It is to be noted that the masses of the neutral atoms O^{16} and H^1 are used here (and will be used throughout the book). The justification for this is that the masses of 8 electrons of the O^{16} are canceled in the calculation by the masses of the 8 electrons of the hydrogen. (The change in the mass of the 8 electrons, due to their stronger binding around the O^{16} nucleus, is beyond the experimental error in the mass determinations.)

Two quantities useful in describing the binding energy of nuclei are:

$$\text{Mass excess} \equiv \Delta \equiv M - A$$

$$\text{Packing fraction} \equiv f \equiv \Delta/A$$

The packing fraction is plotted as a function of A in Fig. 1.

Consider now a nuclear reaction

$$^3\text{Li}^7 + {}^1\text{H}^1 \rightarrow {}^2\text{He}^4 + {}^2\text{He}^4$$

Both the mass number and charge balance. In addition, mass-energy conservation must hold. The balance sheet is as follows:

Initial mass:

$M(^3\text{Li}^7)$	$= 7.01822$
$M(^1\text{H}^1)$	$= 1.00812$
Total	$= 8.02634$

Final mass:

$2M(^2\text{He}^4)$	$= 8.00780$

Mass decrease $= 0.01854$ mass unit

To get the energy equivalent in electron volts $\Delta E = \Delta M c^2$, the conversion factor

$$1 \text{ milli-mass unit} = 0.931 \text{ Mev}$$

is used (see Nuclear Physics A,* p. 86). This gives 17.26 Mev which is released as kinetic energy. If the $^3\text{Li}^7$ and $^1\text{H}^1$ had little

* The three papers by H. A. Bethe in *Reviews of Modern Physics*, namely, Vol. 8, 83, 1936 (with R. F. Bacher); Vol. 9, 69, 1937; and Vol. 9, 245, 1937 (with M. S. Livingston), are hereinafter referred to as Nuclear Physics A, B, and C.

velocity, the α-particles will fly off in nearly opposite directions, each carrying 8.63-Mev kinetic energy. Systematic observations of reactions such as this have verified the Einstein relation very accurately over a great range of nuclear phenomena and are one of the strongest bulwarks of the special theory of relativity. In all nuclear reactions involving heavy particles only, energy has been found to be strictly conserved.

Stability. For a nucleus to be stable it must have a mass which is less than the combined masses of any pair of nuclei made by subdividing it. For example, $^3Li^7$ is stable against the subdivision

$$^3Li^7 \rightarrow {}^2He^4 + {}^1H^3$$

because $M(^3Li^7) = 7.01822$ and $M(^2He^4) + M(^1H^3) = 4.00390 + 3.01702 = 7.02092$. $^2He^5$ is unstable because the decomposition

$$He^5 \rightarrow He^4 + n^0$$

is energetically possible. The mass of He^5 can be found by studying the reaction

$$Li^7 + H^2 \rightarrow He^4 + He^5$$

Knowing the masses $M(Li^7)$, $M(H^2)$, and $M(He^4)$, and measuring the kinetic energy and momentum of Li^7, H^2, and He^4, the mass of He^5 can be determined. It is 5.0137 mass units. This is 0.9 milli-mass unit greater than $M(He^4) + M(n^0)$. (There is the possibility that the measured mass of He^5 might not be for the ground state, but in all known nuclear reactions involving heavy particles, whenever a reaction yields an excited state, it also yields the ground state. Since the experiment gives a unique mass it is presumed to correspond to the ground state.) Li^5 is unstable to the decomposition $Li^5 \rightarrow {}^2He^4 + H^1$, and Be^8 to the decomposition $Be^8 \rightarrow He^4 + He^4$. This explains the absence of nuclei of mass numbers 5 and 8 which was mentioned above.

Fundamental Particles in Nuclei. Present ideas are that a nucleus is composed of protons and neutrons: Z protons and $(A - Z)$ neutrons. This replaces older conceptions which let a nucleus be made up of protons and electrons. Thus the binding energy of any nucleus will be $M - (A - Z)M(n^0) - (Z)M(H^1)$.

II. THE SIZE OF NUCLEI

METHODS OF DETERMINING SIZE

There are four main methods of determining the size of nuclei.

1. *Lifetimes for Alpha Radioactivity.* Nuclei with a mass number A greater than 208 are found to emit helium nuclei (α-particles) spontaneously according to the equation

$$Z^A \rightarrow (Z-2)^{A-4} + {}^2\mathrm{He}^4$$

The lifetimes of such radioactive nuclei are found to vary over a wide range and to depend strongly on the amount of energy available for the reaction. This is illustrated by the tabulation:

Element	Lifetime	Energy	Radius
Th	2×10^{10} years	4.34 Mev	8.7×10^{-13} cm
RaC'	10^{-3} second	7.83 Mev	9.4×10^{-13} cm

A factor of 2 in energy is thus seen to be equivalent to a factor of the order of 10^{20} in lifetime. This strong energy dependence

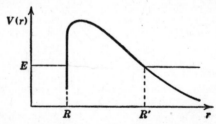

FIG. 2. Nuclear potential barrier for α-particles.

was explained by Gamow, and simultaneously by Gurney and Condon, to result from the necessity of the α-particle to penetrate a potential barrier before escaping.

At large distances, the potential is that due to Coulomb repulsion between a nucleus of charge $Z-2$ and one of charge 2. At some very short distance, attractive nuclear forces predominate. The potential as a function of separation r between α-particle and residual nucleus is shown in Fig. 2.

6

The inner radius R at which nuclear forces come into play is defined as the nuclear radius. The probability of an α-particle of energy E penetrating the barrier is given by the Wentzel-Brillouin-Kramers method to be proportional to

$$\exp\left[-\frac{2}{\hbar}\int_R^{R'}\sqrt{2M[V(r)-E]}\,dr\right] \tag{1}$$

This is called the transmission coefficient of the barrier.

Comparison of this formula with experimental lifetimes shows that the enormous variation of lifetime with energy is indeed explained by the theory, using very nearly the same radius for all radioactive nuclei. Moreover, the formula permits a determination of nuclear radii. With three exceptions, all of these lie between 8.4 and 9.8×10^{-13} cm. The success of this first application of quantum mechanics to nuclear phenomena gives us confidence in the general use of quantum mechanics for the description of the motion of heavy particles in nuclei.

2. *Cross Section for Fast Neutrons.* The cross section presented by a nucleus to a fast neutron should approach the geometrical cross section for neutron wave lengths small compared to the nuclear radius: $\lambda/2\pi = \lambdabar \ll R$. (This condition is required in order to make a geometrical point of view permissible.) Under this condition every neutron hitting the nucleus strongly interacts with it and should, therefore, cause some reaction.

The geometrical cross section is πR^2, thus permitting a calculation of the nuclear radius from the observed cross sections for fast neutrons. ("Shadow scattering" must be excluded.)

Heavy elements Pb, U, etc., are found to have cross sections of about 3×10^{-24} cm^2 so that their radius is 10^{-12} cm. Middle elements such as Fe are found to have cross sections of about 1×10^{-24} cm^2, corresponding to radii of about 6×10^{-13} cm.

3. *Electrostatic Interaction of Protons in the Nucleus.* If the binding energies of a pair of nuclei which differ only in the interchange of neutrons and protons are compared, a difference in binding energy which increases with the charge of the nuclei is found. Examples of such "mirror" nuclei are:

$$^1\text{H}^3 \; ^2\text{He}^3; \quad ^3\text{Li}^7 \; ^4\text{Be}^7; \quad ^5\text{B}^{11} \; ^6\text{C}^{11};$$

$$^6\text{C}^{13} \; ^7\text{N}^{13}; \quad ^7\text{N}^{15} \; ^8\text{O}^{15}; \quad ^{14}\text{Si}^{29} \; ^{15}\text{P}^{29}$$

If neutrons and protons a⁄e assumed to be the same as far as nuclear forces alone are c⁄ncerned, this difference in binding energy is the result of the additional Coulomb repulsion of the extra proton in the field of the original Z protons. To calculate this, all protons are assumed to be uniformly distributed over a sphere of radius R. Then the extra Coulomb repulsion energy due to the replacement of a neutron by a proton is

$$C = \tfrac{6}{5} Ze^2/R \tag{2}$$

Using this formula and the observed differences in binding energy to determine nuclear radii leads to the empirical formula

$$R = 1.5 \times 10^{-13} A^{\frac{1}{3}} \text{ cm} \tag{3}$$

This is a reasonable result since it implies that there is roughly a constant volume for each nuclear particle. It further supports the original assumption that neutrons and protons have similar nuclear forces. Furthermore, extrapolation of the result to high atomic weight is in very good agreement with radii given by the α-activity and the neutron-scattering method.

4. *Cross Sections for Nuclear Reactions Involving Charged Particles.* These reactions also involve the penetration of a barrier. The cross sections, in comparison with neutron cross sections, give the transmission of the barrier. Nuclear radii can be computed from these transmissions, thus extending the "α-activity method" down to non-radioactive nuclei. The results are in agreement with the empirical formula 3.

CONCLUSIONS REGARDING THE CONSTITUENTS OF NUCLEI

The size of nuclei is a strong argument for the presence of protons and neutrons in the nucleus rather than protons and electrons. The de Broglie wave length of a neutron or a proton in the nucleus can be estimated to be:

$$\lambda = \hbar/p = \hbar/\sqrt{2ME} \sim 1.5 \times 10^{-13} \text{ cm} \tag{4}$$

if we use a kinetic energy E of 8 Mev, in other words of the same order of magnitude as the binding energy per nucleon.

On the other hand, for electrons at this relativistic energy, we would have

$$\lambdabar = \hbar/p \approx \hbar c/E \sim 2.5 \times 10^{-12} \text{ cm} \tag{5}$$

Thus the neutron or proton wave length is of the right order of magnitude for the space available in the nucleus, whereas the electron wave length is much too large.

Another argument against the presence of electrons is the long lifetime found for β-emitting nuclei. The long lifetime is not explainable by a potential barrier, because the low electron mass would result in a high transmission coefficient in any barrier the width of which is reasonable considering the nuclear size. Moreover, no barrier at all should be expected for electrons because they are attracted by the Coulomb field of the nucleus. Finally, great difficulties would be encountered in any relativistic theory of the electron if barriers of height greater than $2mc^2$ (m = electron mass) were assumed.

III. BETA DISINTEGRATION (DESCRIPTIVE)

1. Nuclei are found in nature (and more can be produced artificially) that emit electrons spontaneously according to the reaction scheme:

$$Z^A \rightarrow (Z + 1)^A + \beta^-$$

The energy available for such a reaction is given by:

$$E = M_n(Z^A) - M_n(Z + 1)^A - m(e)$$
$$= M_a(Z^A) - Zm(e) - M_a(Z + 1)^A + (Z + 1)m(e) - m(e)$$
$$= M_a(Z^A) - M_a(Z + 1)^A \tag{6}$$

where the subscript n denotes nuclear mass and the subscript a atomic mass.

2. Artificially radioactive substances are found which emit positrons:

$$Z^A \rightarrow (Z - 1)^A + \beta^+$$

Writing out the mass-energy equation as before, it is now found that the energy available is

$$E = M_a(Z^A) - M_a(Z - 1)^A - 2m(e) \tag{7}$$

3. Whenever positron emission occurs, electron capture (usually from the K-shell) can also occur, according to the scheme:

$$Z^A + \beta_K^- \rightarrow (Z - 1)^A$$

leading to the same nucleus. Clearly, the energy available for electron capture is

$$E = M_a(Z^A) - M_a(Z - 1)^A \tag{8}$$

or greater than that available for positron emission by 2 electron masses.

Whenever energy is available for a disintegration process, i.e., $E > 0$, this process can be expected to occur—although, in some cases, the probability will be small due to nuclear selection rules.

It should be noted that the energies just computed neglect the binding energies of the electrons in the atom since these are usually small compared with nuclear binding energies. This assumption, of course, is not completely valid for K-electron capture in the heavier elements but becomes increasingly valid for electrons from the outer shells of the atom.

STABILITY OF ISOBARS

The criteria for β-decay account for the rules for existence of isobars in nature: of two nuclei Z^A and $(Z - 1)^A$, the one with greater atomic mass is unstable against β-decay to the other. This makes the existence in nature of isobars of neighboring Z unlikely. There are, however, many (about fifty) isobar pairs in nature of the type Z^A and $(Z - 2)^A$, with both Z and A even. The intermediate nucleus, $(Z - 1)^A$, of odd charge, decays to one or the other of its neighbors, or sometimes to both.

The occurrence of the exceptional pairs Z^A, $(Z - 1)^A$ is accounted for by a very long half-life of the unstable partner for β-decay. These pairs are discussed in the following.

$$A = 40 \qquad {}^{18}A^{40} \; {}^{19}K^{40} \xrightarrow[\beta^-]{} {}^{20}Ca^{40}$$
$$\text{Spin 0} \quad \text{Spin 4} \qquad \text{Spin 0}$$

K^{40} occurs only in 1 part to 4000 of stable K. It has a half-life of about 4.5×10^{16} seconds for decay by β^--emission to Ca^{40}. Its decay to A^{40} has not been observed. The long half-life is accounted for in the theory by showing that the probability of such a large nuclear spin change is very small.

$$A = 87 \qquad {}^{37}Rb^{87} \xrightarrow[\beta^-]{} {}^{38}Sr^{87}$$
$$\text{Spin } 3/2 \qquad \text{Spin } 9/2$$

Each of these elements is a common isotope; the half-life is 6×10^{18} seconds. The radioactivity of Rb has been known for a considerable time. The identification of the radioactive isotope came from the discovery of a small quantity of Sr^{87}, without any other isotope of Sr, in a mineral containing Rb. The long half-life is again accounted for by large nuclear spin change.

Some of the details of the remaining exceptional isobar pairs are not known.

$$A = 113 \qquad {}^{48}Cd^{113} \rightarrow {}^{49}In^{113}$$

It is known that Cd^{113} has spin $1/2$ and In^{113} has spin $9/2$. The large spin change will undoubtedly correspond to a long lifetime.

The disintegration has not been observed here but the high relative abundance of Cd^{113} and the low relative abundance of In^{113} lead to the conclusion that the transformation is probably K-electron capture by In^{113}.

$$A = 115 \qquad {}^{49}In^{115} \rightarrow {}^{50}Sn^{115}$$

The spin of ${}^{49}In^{115}$ is known to be $9\!/_2$; the spin of ${}^{50}Sn^{115}$ is unknown.

$$A = 123 \qquad {}^{51}Sb^{123} \rightarrow {}^{52}Te^{123}$$

The spin of ${}^{51}Sb^{123}$ is $7\!/_2$; the spin of ${}^{52}Te^{123}$ is unknown. In these two pairs, the high value of the known spin makes it probable that, like the known decay processes just referred to, they have long half-lives because of large spin change.

$$A = 187 \qquad {}^{76}Os^{187} \rightarrow {}^{75}Re^{187}$$

This was the first case in which K-capture (by osmium) was actually observed with a natural isotope (as described in *Nature*, 1945).

APPLICATION TO NUCLEAR ABUNDANCE

In Chapter I it was stated that (1) with very few exceptions the stable nuclei with even A had even Z, and (2) the number of species with even A is larger than with odd A. These facts can now be interpreted. It need only be assumed that for even A the energy (atomic mass) is generally smaller for even Z than for odd Z, whereas for odd A there is no such alternation. Then, a nucleus with even A and odd Z will have an atomic mass greater than one or both of its neighbors and may decay to one or both by β-emission and K-capture. This explains rule 1. Both neighbors of the above-mentioned nucleus, however, may be stable, giving the possibility of isobars differing by *two* units of nuclear charge: for even A, there are therefore many pairs of isobars. For any given odd A, on the other hand, there is usually only *one* possible nucleus—either of even Z or of odd Z. This explains rule 2.

Moreover, for a given even Z, the isotopes with even A are more stable and therefore generally extend farther away from the mean value of the mass number. For instance, xenon has the stable isotopes

$A =$	124	126	128	130	132	134	136
			129	131			

IV. FURTHER FACTS ON NUCLEAR DISINTEGRATIONS

γ-RAYS

Nuclei not only emit particles (heavy particles and electrons), but also γ-radiation (light quanta). Such emission is possible only when a nucleus goes from an excited energy state to a lower energy state. The half-lives for dipole radiation (nuclear spin change $\Delta I = 0$, or ± 1) are generally of the order of 10^{-17} second to about 10^{-13} second. Quadrupole radiation ($\Delta I = \pm 2$) also often gives lifetimes of the order of 10^{-13} second, in contrast to the situation in atomic spectra where the lifetimes are much longer for quadrupole than for dipole radiation. However, for lower frequency ($h\nu \approx 20$–200 kev) the lifetime for quadrupole radiation is much longer (10^{-10} to 10^{-3} second). For octopole radiation ($\Delta I = \pm 3$) of similarly low energy the half-life may be from 10^{-5} second to several hours, and for $\Delta I = \pm 4$ from 1 second to many years.

When the lowest excited state of a nucleus has a sufficiently different spin from the ground state that the half-life is very long, the excited state is called metastable, or an isomer of the nucleus. The excited isomer is usually denoted by an asterisk; In* was the first observed.

SUMMARY OF DECAY PROCESSES

Consider a nucleus Z^A in some quantum state.

1. It may be unstable to the emission of heavy particles.

Neutrons. The lifetime will be 10^{-21} to 10^{-18} second, except if the energy available to the neutron is exceedingly small (a few electron volts), when it may be as long as 10^{-12} second. A lower limit can be calculated roughly by finding the time for a neutron of average velocity to travel the nuclear radius, i.e., 10^{-12} cm/$(10^9$ cm per second$) = 10^{-21}$ second; thus a nucleus unstable to neutron emission is scarcely observable.

Protons. If the protons have enough energy to go over the Coulomb barrier, the lifetimes are about equal to the lifetimes for neutrons. If the protons must penetrate the Coulomb barrier because their kinetic energies are low, then the Gamow penetration factor leads to much longer lifetimes.

α-Particles. In general, the same rule applies as for protons except that for a given energy, longer half-lives are to be expected because of the larger mass and charge of the α-particle. In particular, to get observable half-lives (as short as 10^{14} years), the energy of the α-particle in the nucleus must be greater than 3.5 Mev for $Z = 92$, greater than 1 kev for $Z = 4$.

2. It may be unstable to the emission of light quanta. Half-lives are in general from 10^{-17} second to 10^{-10} second, but occasionally (in isomers, for instance) run from seconds to years.

3. Emission of β-rays or K-electron capture. Half-lives are 0.02 second to 10^{11} years, and more.

Thus the unstable nuclei can be put into three groups:

Group I. Lives unobservably short:

First, from 10^{-21} to 10^{-18} second: The very unstable nuclei He^5 and Li^5 in their ground states, or any nucleus in an excited state of high enough energy so that a fast neutron, fast proton, or α-particle can be emitted.

Second, from 10^{-17} to about 10^{-6} second: Nearly all excited states of nuclei not contained in the group just described. These nuclei will in general lose their energy by γ-emission, or sometimes by emission of slow neutrons, protons, etc.

Group II. Lives observable (10^{-6} second to 10^{12} years): Nearly all β-radioactive nuclei, many α-radioactive ones, and many "nuclear isomers" emitting γ-rays.

Group III. Lives unobservably long: If a radioactive nucleus has a half-life greater than about 10^{14} years, its activity will be unobservable. For α-radioactivity, this sets a lower limit on the energy of the α-particles which will make the activity observable for a given nuclear charge Z as follows:

Z	=	10	30	50	70	90	
$E_{min.}$ (α)	=	0.13	0.8	1.7	2.7	3.7	Mev

V. SPIN AND STATISTICS

SPIN

Each nucleus has an intrinsic angular momentum which interacts with angular momenta of electrons or other nuclei. It is measured in units of $\hbar$ and, according to quantum mechanics, can take on only integral or half-integral values. Three methods of determining nuclear spin are:

1. *Hyperfine Structure of Spectra.* The interaction of the magnetic moments of the electrons and the nucleus may separate in energy the states of the atom corresponding to various values of the angular momentum and result in splitting of spectral lines.

2. *Band Spectra.* Intensity variations of alternate lines in band spectra of molecules with identical nuclei yield nuclear spins.

3. *Molecular Beams.* The magnetic moment associated with the nuclear spin is used to perform a Stern-Gerlach experiment, splitting a beam of atoms in an inhomogeneous magnetic field according to the component of their nuclear magnetic moments in the direction of the field. First measurements were by Stern and Rabi. Important modifications were made by Rabi, by Purcell, and by Bloch and Hansen and their collaborators.

Table 2 gives the observed spins of some nuclei.

TABLE 2

SAMPLE SPINS

Electron	$\frac{1}{2}$	Li^6	1	O^{16}	0
H^1	$\frac{1}{2}$	Li^7	$\frac{3}{2}$		
H^2	1	C^{12}	0		
He^4	0	N^{14}	1		

Nuclear Constituents. These observed spin values are another reason for rejecting a nuclear model composed of electrons and protons. Such a model for the nucleus Z^A has A protons and $A - Z$ electrons or $2A - Z$ particles. On this basis nuclei with odd Z (and therefore an odd total number of particles) should have half-integer spin and nuclei with even Z integer or zero spin. $^7N^{14}$

15

with spin 1 was the first contradiction found, but there are many more, e.g.,

$$^1\mathrm{H}^2, \,^3\mathrm{Li}^6 \qquad \text{have spin 1}$$

$$^{48}\mathrm{Cd}^{111}, \,^{48}\mathrm{Cd}^{113} \text{ have spin } \tfrac{1}{2}$$

On the other hand, the model $Z^A = (A - Z)$ neutrons $+ Z$ protons gives A particles in all, and, assuming half-integer spin for the neutron, the rule becomes: even A, integer or zero spin; odd A, half-integer spin. This agrees with all measured spins.

STATISTICS

Identical particles obey either Fermi statistics or Bose statistics, that is, a wave function $\psi(P_1, P_2)$, depending on the space and spin coordinates P_1 and P_2 of particles 1 and 2, will be either symmetrical or antisymmetrical under exchange of P_1 and P_2

$$\psi(P_2, P_1) = \begin{cases} +\psi(P_1 P_2) \text{ Bose} \\ -\psi(P_1 P_2) \text{ Fermi} \end{cases} \tag{9}$$

Electrons obey Fermi statistics. To determine the statistics of nuclei, we shall investigate how an exchange of identical nuclei will affect the sign of the wave function for a molecule.

Consider a diatomic molecule with identical nuclei. Its wave function may be written

$$\psi = \psi_{\text{elec.}} \varphi_{\text{vibration}} \rho_{\text{rotation}} \sigma_{\text{nucl. spin}} \tag{10}$$

Let the operation of exchanging nuclear coordinates and spins be denoted by P. Then

$$P\psi_{\text{elec.}} = \pm \psi_{\text{elec.}}$$

The sign may be plus or minus; it is known from molecular spectroscopy and is usually $+$ for the ground state. Further,

$$P\varphi_{\text{vibration}} = +\varphi_{\text{vibration}}$$

because φ depends on R (the distance of the nuclei) alone and $PR = R$.

Now

$$\rho = P_l^m(\cos\theta)e^{im\phi}$$

$P_l^m(x)$ is an associated Legendre polynomial, and θ and ϕ are the polar coordinates of the two nuclei. P means replacing the direction θ, ϕ by the opposite direction, i.e.,

$$\theta \rightarrow \pi - \theta$$

$$\varphi \rightarrow \pi + \varphi$$

Now

$$P_l{}^m(\pi - \theta) = (-1)^{l+m} P_l{}^m(\theta).$$

Further,

$$e^{im(\phi + \pi)} = (-1)^m e^{im\phi}$$

so that

$$P\rho = (-1)^{l+m} P_l{}^m(\cos \theta)(-1)^m e^{im\phi} = (-1)^l \rho \qquad (11)$$

Thus ρ is symmetrical for even l and antisymmetrical for odd l.

The analysis of $P\sigma_{\text{nucl. spin}}$ can be carried out for arbitrary spin but is particularly simple for spin zero in which case $P\sigma_{\text{nucl. spin}} = +\sigma_{\text{nucl. spin}}$. Thus for spin zero (and symmetrical $\psi_{\text{elec.}}$), the total wave function ψ is antisymmetrical for odd l and symmetrical for even l. Now the nuclei must certainly obey either Bose or Fermi statistics. Therefore, either only the states with even l, or only those with odd l, can exist. Evidence for this conclusion is obtained from the band spectra. These show indeed that if the nuclei have spin zero, every second rotational state of the molecule is absent. Indeed, it is found in every instance that only the *even* rotational states exist, indicating that all the nuclei of zero spin (which have been found previously to have even A) obey Bose statistics. Similarly, it has been found that *all* nuclei of even A (including those with a spin that is not zero) obey Bose statistics and all those of odd A obey Fermi statistics.

This result throws light on the nature and *statistics of the elementary particles* in the nucleus. Suppose each elementary particle obeys Fermi statistics, then ψ must be antisymmetrical to interchange of a pair of elementary particles. Therefore, if each of the two identical nuclei contains an even number of particles the exchange of the nuclei is equivalent to an even number of changes of sign; and ψ must be symmetrical to an interchange of nuclei (Bose statistics); if each nucleus contains an odd number of particles then exchange of the nuclei is equivalent to an odd number of changes of sign, i.e., ψ is antisymmetrical to nuclear interchange (Fermi statistics).

Now it was found experimentally that nuclei with even A obey Bose statistics, those with odd A Fermi statistics. This can be explained if the total number of elementary particles in a nucleus is A—as is the case if neutrons and protons are considered the fundamental particles—and if, further, each of the elementary particles obeys Fermi statistics. This proves that the neutron must obey Fermi statistics, just as the proton for which this fact is known experimentally. The electron-proton hypothesis fails again because, in this case, the number of elementary particles is $2A - Z$, so that nuclei with even/odd Z would have to obey Bose/Fermi statistics, whereas A rather than Z was found to be the actual criterion.

NUCLEI OF NON-ZERO SPIN

A nucleus of total angular momentum I can have a component M in any prescribed direction, taking any of the values $I, I - 1$, $\cdots$, $-I$ a total of $2I + 1$ states. For two identical nuclei $(2I + 1)^2$ wave functions of the form $\psi_{M_1}(A)\psi_{M_2}(B)$ can be constructed. If the two nuclei are identical, these simple products must be replaced by linear combinations of these products which are symmetric or antisymmetric for interchange of the nuclei.

If $M_1 = M_2$ the products themselves are $(2I + 1)$ symmetric wave functions. The remaining $(2I + 1)(2I)$ functions where M_1 and M_2 are unequal have the form $\psi_{M_1}(A)\psi_{M_2}(B)$ and $\psi_{M_2}(A)\psi_{M_1}(B)$. Each such pair is to be replaced by one symmetric and one antisymmetric wave function of the form

$$\psi_{M_1}(A)\psi_{M_2}(B) \pm \psi_{M_2}(A)\psi_{M_1}(B) \tag{12}$$

Thus half of the $2I(2I + 1)$ functions are antisymmetric, giving $I(2I + 1)$ antisymmetric functions. A similar number of symmetric functions exist, to which the $(2I + 1)$ symmetric functions with $M_1 = M_2$ must be added. Thus the ratio of the number of symmetric to antisymmetric functions is

$$\frac{(I + 1)(2I + 1)}{I(2I + 1)} = \frac{I + 1}{I} \tag{13}$$

If the electronic wave function for the molecule is symmetric, it was shown on page 17 that interchange of nuclei produces a factor $(-1)^l$ in the total molecular wave function, where l is the rotational quantum number. Thus, if the nuclei obey Bose statistics, symmetric nuclear spin functions must be combined with even l rotational states, and antisymmetric spins with odd l. Because of the statistical weights attached to the spin states the intensity of even rotational lines will be $(I + 1)/I$ as great as that of neighboring odd rotational lines.

For Fermi statistics of the nuclei, the spin and the rotational states combine in a manner opposite to that previously stated, and the *odd* rotational lines are more intense in the ratio $(I + 1)/I$.

Thus, by determining which lines are more intense, even or odd,

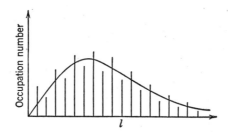

FIG. 3.   Intensity alternation in band spectra.

the nuclear statistics is determined, and by measuring the ratio of intensities of adjacent lines the nuclear spin is obtained.

The reason why adjacent lines must be compared is that the rotational lines vary in intensity with l (neglecting nuclear spin), according to the occupation numbers of the rotational states; in other words, according to a Boltzmann distribution

$$(2l + 1) \exp\left[-E(l)/(kT)\right] \qquad (14)$$

where $E(l) = B\, l(l + 1)$, and B is a constant (about 0.01 ev in H_2).

This Boltzmann distribution provides a smooth intensity variation about which the even and the odd states alternate in intensity (Fig. 3).

The experimental results of band spectra measurements, as already pointed out, are that nuclei of even A obey Bose statistics and nuclei of odd A obey Fermi statistics. Experimental determinations of nuclear spin are tabulated in the Appendix. One empirical rule from these data is that, with no known exceptions, all nuclei of even Z and even A have total nuclear spin zero.

VI. BETA DISINTEGRATION AND THE NEUTRINO

Negative β-disintegration consists in the conversion of a neutron into a proton and an electron. Since all three particles are assumed to have spin $\frac{1}{2}$ and Fermi statistics, this reaction will not conserve spin and statistics unless it is assumed that an additional particle of spin $\frac{1}{2}$ and Fermi statistics is emitted. To conserve charge this particle must be neutral. It is also clear that its mass must be small, and it is therefore called the *neutrino* (Italian for "the small neutral one").

DISTRIBUTION OF ELECTRON ENERGIES

The emitted β-particles are found to have a continuous distribution of energies, up to a certain maximum E_0, rather than a single energy (Fig. 4). The neutrino is therefore also needed to

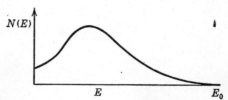

Fig. 4. Energy distribution in β-spectrum.

conserve energy; it is assumed to take the remaining energy, $E_0 - E$, where E is the electron energy. This hypothesis is strongly supported by the fact that the maximum electron energy is found within experimental error to be equal to the energy available for the reaction, as determined from mass data. This shows also that the neutrino mass must be assumed negligible.

Experimental data supporting this assertion may be found, for instance, in the β-disintegration of N^{13} into C^{13} with a maximum positron energy of 1.20 Mev.

The mass difference between N^{13} and C^{13} was determined by measuring the threshold of the reaction (Haxby, Shoupp, Stevens, and Wells, Phys. Rev. **58,** 1035, 1940):

$$C^{13} + H^1 \rightarrow N^{13} + n.$$

The incident proton energy for threshold was measured and corrected to center of mass coordinates by the factor 13/14. The mass-energy equation then became:

$$2.98 \text{ Mev} + C^{13} + H^1 = N^{13} + n \tag{15}$$

or

$$N^{13} - C^{13} = 2.98 - (n - H^1)$$

$$= 2.98 - 0.75$$

$$N^{13} - C^{13} = 2.23 \text{ Mev}$$

where a neutron-proton mass difference of 0.75 Mev is used.

According to equation 7, the energy available for positron emission is the difference in mass $N^{13} - C^{13}$, minus the mass of 2 electrons, so that

$$E \text{ available} = 2.23 - 2(0.51) = 1.21 \text{ Mev} \tag{16}$$

This checks with the maximum positron energy and proves that the neutrino mass must be small if not zero.

EXPERIMENTAL EVIDENCE FOR THE NEUTRINO

The only process which a free neutrino can be expected to cause *with certainty* is the inverse β-process which is fundamentally (letting ν indicate the neutrino) of the form

$$n + \nu \rightarrow H^1 + \beta^-$$

Actually, to observe this process, it is necessary, of course, to use neutrons bound in some nucleus, for instance:

$$Li^7 + \nu \rightarrow Be^7 + \beta^-$$

This process can occur only if the incident neutrinos have sufficient energy to supply the mass difference between Be^7 and Li^7.

In any case the cross section for such a reaction would be extremely small; its order of magnitude is given by the cross section for striking the nucleus (about 10^{-24} cm^2) and the probability of β-decay within a nucleus (about 10^{-20}), so that the cross section would be of the order of 10^{-44} cm^2, or completely unobservable.

Recoil. The most likely way of verifying the neutrino existence is to obtain further evidence for its participation in β-emission.

For example, the neutrino energy can be determined in two ways: first, by measuring the electron energy and subtracting it from the total energy available, and second, by measuring the electron and nuclear *momentum* and using conservation of momentum to obtain the neutrino momentum and energy:

$$E(\nu) = E \text{ (available)} - E(e)$$

$$p(\nu) = p \text{ (nucleus)} + p(e) \tag{17}$$

$$E(\nu) = cp(\nu)$$

where c is the velocity of light (and of the neutrino).

This method, unfortunately, requires measurement of both the nuclear recoil energy and its direction with respect to the electron momentum. Both of these are very difficult measurements to make because of the small recoil energy.

A method which avoids these difficulties (J. Allen, Phys. Rev. **61**, 692, 1942) is to use K-capture by a light nucleus:

$$\text{Be}^7 + \beta_K \rightarrow \text{Li}^7 + \nu$$

Since the K-electron has negligible momentum, the momentum of the recoil nucleus will be equal to that of the neutrino. Further, the emitted neutrinos are monochromatic, having an energy equal to the difference in mass available. The recoil energy can thus be easily computed (p = neutrino momentum):

$$E \text{ (recoil)} = \frac{p^2}{2M} = \frac{[E(\nu)/c]^2}{2M}$$

$$= \frac{[M(\text{Be}^7) - M(\text{Li}^7)]^2 c^4}{2Mc^2} \tag{18}$$

Using $\Delta M = 0.85$ Mev, and M = mass of Li^7, we get E (recoil) = 45 volts.

The measured recoil energies had various values up to a maximum of 45 volts. The values less than 45 volts may be explained by a loss in energy of the recoil nuclei on leaving the beryllium layer.

Further evidence for the existence of the neutrino comes from the detailed theory of β-disintegration that is described in Chapter XVI.

B. QUANTITATIVE THEORY OF NUCLEAR FORCES

VII. PHYSICAL PROPERTIES OF PROTON, NEUTRON, AND DEUTERON

The theory of nuclei is to be contrasted with the theory of atoms. In the latter, the principal force between the constituent particles, electrons and nuclei, was known when the theory got under way, and the problem was to find the proper mechanics to describe the motion of those particles under the given force; quantum mechanics is the answer to this problem. In nuclei, there are good reasons to believe that quantum mechanics is correct (the success of the Gamow theory of α-particle decay is one example), but the forces are unknown.

In investigating these forces, the crucial test of any theory is the deuteron, which is the simplest stable combination of the heavy particles (neutrons and protons) which compose nuclei. The position of the deuteron problem in nuclear theory is similar to that of the problem of the hydrogen atom in atomic theory. It tests the theory without aggravating the computational situation which is already complicated enough in the theory of the simplest nuclei.

First of all, a tabulation of existing information concerning the proton, the neutron, and the deuteron may be helpful.

PROTON

Charge: e (makes it easily observable by its ionization in matter).
Mass: 1.00812 (includes mass of an electron).
Range-kinetic energy relationship.

Protons of a given energy have a definite range in matter of given density and atomic number (see Nuclear Physics C, p. 269, for a graph). For example, 10-Mev protons have a range of about 1 mm of water.

Spin: ½.
Statistics: Fermi.
Magnetic moment: +2.7896 nuclear magnetons.

The most accurate measurement is by Rabi, Kellogg, Ramsey, and Zacharias (Phys. Rev. **56**, 728, 1939). This magnetic moment is different from 1 nuclear magneton ($= e\hbar/2Mc$), which is the magnetic moment which it would have if it obeyed the Dirac equation. The meson theory of nuclear forces gives a qualitative but as yet no quantitative account of the proton moment. The positive sign of the magnetic moment indicates that it points in the same direction as the spin or mechanical moment, which is what would be expected from a rotating positive distribution of charge.

NEUTRON

Charge: 0.

Mass: 1.00893.

No range-kinetic energy relationship.

The neutron can only ionize matter by means of its small magnetic moment, which gives practically no ionization at all. It is detectable only by means of the products of its collisions with nuclei. Instead of a range-energy relationship the neutron has a mean free path (of 2 to 20 cm in solids, depending on the velocity and material). The neutron diffuses through matter.

Spin: half-integral. (Reasons for presuming the spin to be precisely ½ are given below.)

Statistics: Fermi.

Magnetic moment: -1.9103 ± 0.0012 nuclear magnetons.

The first measurement was by Alvarez and Bloch (Phys. Rev. **57**, 111, 1940). A beam of neutrons was passed through a block of iron saturated by a magnetic field. This polarized the neutrons with magnetic moments parallel to the field. Then, still in a constant steady field but now out of the iron, it was acted on by a radio-frequency field perpendicular to the steady field. Finally it passed through another iron block, the analyzer, with its saturated magnetic field parallel to the former one, and into a neutron detector. If the radio frequency were close to the Larmor precession frequency of the neutron, the beam would be strongly depolarized in the radio-frequency field and strongly scattered in the analyzer block. Thus the Larmor precession frequency was the radio frequency at which fewest neutrons were transmitted. The Larmor frequency divided by H, the steady magnetic field, is proportional to the gyromagnetic ratio of the neutron, i.e.,

$$\frac{\nu}{H} \sim \frac{\text{(magnetic moment)}}{\text{(angular momentum)}} \tag{19}$$

The measurement by Alvarez and Bloch gave a value of 1.935 ± 0.02 nuclear magnetons (for a spin of $\frac{1}{2}$).

Recently a much more accurate determination of the neutron moment was made by Arnold and Roberts (Phys. Rev. **70**, 766, 1946). The method was similar to that of Alvarez and Bloch except that the magnetic field was calibrated by a measurement of the proton moment in the same field. The experiment therefore gives directly the ratio of the moments of neutron and proton, which is exactly the quantity needed in the theory (see Chapter VII). The value obtained by Arnold and Roberts is the one given above.

DEUTERON

Charge: e.
Mass: 2.01472 (includes 1 electron).
Spin: 1.
Statistics: Bose.
Magnetic moment: $+0.8565 \pm 0.0004$ nuclear magneton.

All quantities are stated for the ground state of the deuteron. The magnetic-moment measurement is also published in the paper on the proton by Rabi and collaborators (Phys. Rev. **56**, 728, 1939).

In the quantum mechanical description of the deuteron, it is reasonable to assume the ground state to be an S state, i.e., a state of no orbital angular momentum, $L = 0$. This means that the wave function has no angular nodes. (With plausible assumptions on the forces it can be proved theoretically that the ground-state wave function has no nodes whatever.) With $L = 0$, ψ is spherically symmetrical and the angular momentum of the nucleus is entirely attributable to spin. Assuming that the neutron has spin $\frac{1}{2}$, the deuteron spin of 1 implies that the proton and the neutron spins are parallel. In such a case the magnetic moments should also add:

$$\text{Proton moment} = \quad 2.7896 \pm 0.0008.$$

$$\text{Neutron moment} = \quad -1.9103 \pm 0.0012.$$

$$\text{Sum of the two moments} = \quad 0.8793 \pm 0.0015.$$

$$\text{Deuteron moment} = \quad 0.8565 \pm 0.0004.$$

$$\text{Difference} = \quad 0.0228 \pm 0.0016.$$

It is seen that the deuteron moment agrees almost but not quite with the sum of the moments of proton and neutron. The reason for the small difference will be indicated below.

The approximate agreement can only be achieved by assuming, as has been done here, that the neutron spin is ½ and the orbital

TABLE 3

Calculated Magnetic Moment of the Deuteron

A. *If the Neutron Moment Is Negative:*

$S_N =$	½		¾	
$S =$	0	1	1	2
L				
0	—	0.854	−6.232	—
1	0.500	0.677	−2.866	−2.512
2	—	0.323	3.866	−0.504

B. *If the Neutron Moment Is Positive:*

$S_N =$	½		¾	
$S =$	0	1	1	2
L				
0	—	4.721	3.436	—
1	0.500	2.610	1.968	6.190
2	—	−1.6	−0.968	2.397

S_N = assumed spin of the neutron.
S = resultant spin of the deuteron.
L = orbital momentum of the deuteron.
I = total angular momentum = 1. A dash (—) indicates that these combinations cannot lead to $I = 1$.

angular moment of the deuteron is 0. This is shown by Table 3, in which the magnetic moment of the deuteron is calculated for a great number of different assumptions on the neutron spin, the sign of the magnetic moment of the neutron, and the value of L, the orbital momentum in the deuteron ground state. Because these calculations were made before Roberts' experiments, the magnetic moment of the neutron was assumed to be 1.93 rather than 1.91. The results are given in the table.

It is seen that only $S = 1$, $L = 0$ leads to a result that is not very far from the measured one; all other combinations, especially those for $S = \frac{3}{2}$ or for positive neutron moment, are completely different from the measured moment of the deuteron.

Thus the magnetic-moment measurements are good evidence for the following:

1. In the ground state of the deuteron the spins of proton and neutron are parallel (triplet state).

2. The neutron spin is $\frac{1}{2}$.

3. In the ground state of the deuteron the orbital angular momentum is zero (S-state).

Quadrupole moment.   Rabi and his co-workers have shown that the deuteron also possesses an electric quadrupole moment such that it appears as a spheroid prolate along the spin axis:

$$\frac{\overline{z^2}}{\overline{r^2}} = \frac{\text{average } z^2 \text{ for proton}}{\text{average } r^2 \text{ for proton}} = \frac{1}{3} \cdot (1.14) \qquad (20)$$

instead of $\frac{1}{3}$ as it would be for a spherically symmetrical charge distribution: $(\overline{r^2} = \overline{x^2} + \overline{y^2} + \overline{z^2})$. Thus the wave function ψ cannot be independent of the angle θ between the total spin and the line joining the nuclei. If ψ be expanded in spherical harmonics, a dependence such as

$$\psi = u + wP_2(\cos \theta) \qquad (21)$$

must be assumed, where P_2 is a normalized Legendre polynomial. (No P_1 term appears because the electric dipole moment is zero.) In order to obtain the functions u and w, the deuteron problem must be solved with an explicit assumption about the nuclear forces. This was done by Rarita and Schwinger (see Chapter XIII). The most important result of their calculations is the fraction of the time during which the deuteron has orbital moment 2, viz.,

$$p_D = \frac{\int w^2 \, d\tau}{\int u^2 \, d\tau + \int w^2 \, d\tau} = 3.9 \text{ per cent} \qquad (22)$$

Since the deuteron now is no longer perfectly symmetric, its magnetic moment should not be exactly the sum of the moments of proton and neutron. This fact seemed to present a considerable difficulty with the old measurement of the neutron moment by

Alvarez and Bloch. With this measurement the deuteron moment was almost exactly the sum of the neutron and the proton moments. On the other hand, the experimental error was too large to permit definite conclusions.

This situation has been relieved by the work of Arnold and Roberts. According to this measurement, the deuteron moment is smaller than the sum of the moments of the individual particles by 0.0228 ± 0.0016 nuclear magneton. From this figure it is possible to calculate the percentage of time during which the deuteron is in the D state ($L = 2$). If this state were pure, Landé's formula would give for the deuteron moment the value 0.3104, on the basis of the measured moments for proton and neutron. If the fraction of time in the D state is p, the moment should be

$$\mu = 0.8793(1 - p) + 0.3104p \tag{23}$$

Setting this equal to the measured moment, $p = 4.0 \pm 0.3$ per cent is obtained. This value is in excellent agreement with the theoretical value (equation 22); in fact, the agreement is much better than is warranted by the assumptions made in the theory. Relativistic corrections may reduce the value of p deduced from experiment to about 3 per cent (according to calculations of Schwinger).

In order to account for the electric quadrupole moment, forces must be introduced which depend on the angle θ between the line joining the nuclei and the axis of total spin (purely central forces give no mixing of states with different L). These are called tensor forces; Wigner has established their general characteristics. However, in the next few chapters a potential $V(r)$ will be assumed (r distance between nuclei). This will enable a qualitative account of the principal features of the deuteron without giving such fine details as the quadrupole moment.

VIII. GROUND STATE OF THE DEUTERON

Binding Energy. The most important experimental basis for the theory of the deuteron is its binding energy. This was first measured by Chadwick and Goldhaber in 1934, using the photo-disintegration of deuterons by the 2.62-Mev γ-rays from thorium C':

$$H^2 + h\nu \rightarrow H^1 + n \tag{24}$$

This reaction takes place when $h\nu$ is greater than the binding energy of the deuteron; the difference between $h\nu$ and the binding energy appears as kinetic energy of the neutron and the proton. Because the momentum of the γ-ray is so small, the momenta of proton and neutron are very nearly equal and opposite, and since their masses are almost exactly equal, they share the excess energy, $h\nu$ minus binding energy, very nearly equally. The energy E of the proton can be determined by measuring the total ionization it produces or by measuring its range. The binding energy is then $h\nu - 2E$.

One of the best direct measurements of the deuteron binding energy is that of Stetter and Jentschke who (by measuring ionization) obtained a value 2.19 ± 0.03 Mev. (The probable error has been increased somewhat over that given by the authors.) Another accurate determination was made by Wiedenbeck and Marhoefer (Phys. Rev. **67**, 54, 1945), who studied the excitation of the deuteron by γ-rays which were artificially produced by letting high-energy electrons from a Van de Graaff machine fall on a heavy target. The authors observed the yield of neutrons as a function of the electron energy and found a linear relation which they extrapolated to find the threshold. Although plausible, the linear extrapolation does not seem established beyond doubt and the result should, therefore, be stated with a conservative margin of error. It is then 2.185 ± 0.02 Mev. A similar method was used by Myers and Van Atta, and a similar result was obtained by Kimura, using a different method.

Another accurate determination can be obtained by taking the difference in mass of the deuteron and of the free constituent particles. The masses of deuteron and proton are known accurately from mass spectrographic data, and the mass difference of neutron and proton is known accurately from measurements on the reaction chain

$$C^{13}(p, n)N^{13}(\beta^+)C^{13}$$

(see Chapter VI). The equation

Binding energy $= [2M(H^1) + \{M(n) - M(H^1)\} - M(H^2)]$

gives the result 2.19 $\pm$ 0.03 Mev.*

Nature of Forces. In order to discuss the deuteron quantum mechanically, we must know or guess something about the nature of the "nuclear" force holding neutron and proton together. This force cannot be electrical as the neutron is uncharged; nor can it be gravitational, for assuming a gravitational force gives an interaction potential too small by about a factor 10^{38}. So we must accept the nuclear force as a new type of force and try to find out more about it.

We shall first of all assume a central force, i.e., the interaction potential of neutron and proton is some function $V(r)$, where r is the distance between the particles. This is only in slight disagreement with known facts; for a central force would yield a ground state with angular momentum 0, whereas it was shown in Chapter VII, that the deuteron ground state has a small fraction of the state $l = 2$ in addition to the predominant state $l = 0$.

Second, it was shown by Wigner that the nuclear force has a short range. This assumption must be made to explain the low binding energy (2.19 Mev; about 1 Mev per particle) of the deuteron compared to that of H^3 (8.5 Mev; about 3 Mev per particle) and of He^4 (28 Mev; about 7 Mev per particle) which cannot be explained by a long range force (e.g., $V(r) \sim -1/r$). Wigner's argument was essentially that the nuclei with more particles have more nuclear bonds per particle (D^2 has $\frac{1}{2}$, H^3 has $\frac{3}{3}$, He^4 has $\frac{6}{4}$ bonds per particle). This in itself is not sufficient to explain the ratios of binding energy per particle; however, the larger number of bonds per particle in the heavier nuclei causes these particles to be pulled within the (short) range of the nuclear

---

* An exhaustive discussion of the determinations of the binding energy of the deuteron was given by Stevens (Rev. Mod. Phys. **19**, 19, 1947). He adopts as the best value 2.187 $\pm$ 0.011.—*Note added in proof.*

forces a greater percentage of the time, increasing the binding energy by a large amount. Thomas has shown by a rigorous mathematical proof that it is possible to get as large a ratio of the binding energy of H^3 to that of H^2 as desired by choosing the range of forces small enough (and simultaneously adjusting the depth of the hole to yield the correct binding energy). From this argument, one would expect that the binding energy of the deuteron is small compared to the total depth of the potential hole and that the particles in the deuteron spend a great part of the time outside the range of the nuclear forces—i.e., the "radius" of the deuteron is considerably greater than the range of nuclear forces.

Wave Equation. If the potential $V(r)$ is known, the binding energy is determined by the Schrödinger equation

$$\nabla^2\psi(r, \theta, \phi) + (2m/\hbar^2)[E - V(r)]\psi(r, \theta, \phi) = 0 \qquad (25)$$

where r is the distance between neutron and proton and m is the reduced mass

$$m = \frac{M_n M_p}{M_n + M_p} \approx \tfrac{1}{2}M \text{ (of proton or neutron)}$$

E is negative and numerically equal to the binding energy. Conversely, if E is known, equation 25 determines, in principle, *one* parameter relating to $V(r)$.

Since $l = 0$ is being taken for the ground state, ψ must be spherically symmetrical. Making the substitution $\psi = u(r)/r$, equation 25 takes on the simpler form

$$\frac{d^2u}{dr^2} + \frac{M}{\hbar^2}[E - V(r)]u = 0 \qquad (26)$$

We must now assume a shape for the potential function $V(r)$. One shape which certainly represents a short range force and also makes for easy solution of the differential equation is the rectangular potential well shown in Fig. 5. Here there are two parameters, width and depth of the well; since

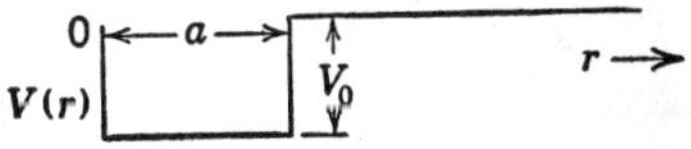

FIG. 5.   Potential "well" of deuteron.

the Schrödinger equation with a given E will determine only one parameter, we expect only to find a relation between V_0 and a, not definite values for them. With $E = -W$, where W is positive, equation 26 becomes for the potential well

$$\frac{d^2u}{dr^2} + \frac{M}{\hbar^2}(V_0 - W)u = 0 \qquad \text{for } r < a \qquad (27a)$$

$$\frac{d^2u}{dr^2} - \frac{M}{\hbar^2}Wu = 0 \qquad \text{for } r > a \qquad (27b)$$

ψ must be continuous and bounded and have a continuous derivative everywhere. Therefore, $u = r\psi$ must have the same continuity condition, must go to zero at $r = 0$, and must not diverge faster than r as $r \to \infty$. To satisfy the conditions at zero and infinity the solution of equation 27 must be

$$u = A \sin kr \qquad \text{for } r < a \qquad (28a)$$

$$u = Be^{-\alpha r} \qquad \text{for } r > a \qquad (28b)$$

where

$$k = \sqrt{M(V_0 - W)}/\hbar \qquad (29a)$$

$$\alpha = \sqrt{MW}/\hbar \qquad (29b)$$

Relation between Range and Depth of Potential. Now, if u and its derivative are continuous, then also the derivative of $\ln u$ must be continuous; applying this at $r = a$ gives

$$k \cot ka = -\alpha \qquad (30)$$

which conveniently does not involve A and B, but only the two unknowns a and V_0, W being known $= 2.19$ Mev. V_0 and a are not restricted further. Thus equation 30 is the relation anticipated between a and V_0.

Equation 30 can be put in a simpler but approximate form. As seen above, W is small compared to V_0 and can be neglected in equation 29a. Thus

$$\cot ka = -\alpha/k \approx -\sqrt{W/V_0} \qquad (31)$$

Thus $\cot ka$ is negative and small in absolute value. Therefore, ka is only slightly larger than $\pi/2$. (ka slightly larger than $3\pi/2$ is not the correct solution, for then there would be a radial node in the wave function ψ at $kr = \pi$, indicating that this ψ is not the lowest energy level, which contradicts our hypothesis.) Using $ka \approx \pi/2$ and again neglecting W in the expression for k gives

$$V_0 a^2 \approx \pi^2 \hbar^2 / 4M \tag{32}$$

Actually $V_0 a^2$ is slightly greater than the quantity on the right; but we can be virtually certain that

$$V_0 a^2 < \pi^2 \hbar^2 / M \quad \text{or} \quad ka < \pi \tag{33}$$

a result which will be needed later. The expression $V_0 a^2$ frequently occurs in nuclear calculations, it often being not necessary to know V_0 and a separately.

Other types of short-range potential function give about the same results as the rectangular well. Potentials of the form e^{-r} and e^{-r^2} are treated in Nuclear Physics A, and the function e^{-r}/r is discussed in Phys. Rev., **53,** 991, 1938, by Göppert-Mayer and Sachs.

Discussion of Wave Function. Another result which does not depend on the form of the potential (as long as it has a short range) is the exponential decrease of $u(r)$ for r greater than the range of nuclear forces. In fact, the function

$$u = Ce^{-\alpha r} \tag{34}$$

is close enough to the true $u(r)$ over the whole region to be useful in many calculations. This is seen clearly by considering Fig. 6.

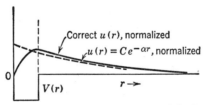

FIG. 6.   Exact and approximate wave functions of deuteron ground state.

The quantity $1/\alpha$ can be taken as a measure of the size of the deuteron. It was shown above that the "radius" of the deuteron is considerably larger than the range of nuclear forces, i.e.:

$$1/\alpha \gg a \tag{35}$$

Thus most of the area under $u(r)$ occurs for $r > a$. Using another form for the potential function changes $u(r)$ appreciably only for

$r < a$. Therefore, independent of the shape of the potential, $Ce^{-\alpha r}$ is close to the true wave function over most of space. This approximation does not give a bounded ψ at $r = 0$; however, ψ is normalizable, and fortunately the main contribution to the normalization integral comes from $r > a$, so the infinity introduces little error.

$$\int \psi^2 \, d\tau = 4\pi \int_0^\infty u^2 \, dr = 4\pi C^2 \int_0^\infty e^{-2\alpha r} \, dr = \frac{2\pi C^2}{\alpha} = 1$$

or

$$C = \sqrt{\alpha/2\pi}$$

Therefore

$$u(r) = \sqrt{\alpha/2\pi} \, e^{-\alpha r} \tag{36}$$

is the normalized approximate form of $u(r)$.

If definite values are assigned to a and V_0, then A and B of the true $u(r)$ given by equation 28 can be found from the continuity condition and normalization. B is a little greater than C of the approximate $u(r)$. In fact,

$$B = \sqrt{\alpha/2\pi}(1 + \tfrac{1}{2}\alpha a) \tag{37}$$

is a good approximation.

Excited States of the Deuteron. On the basis of the preceding theory the possibility of other bound states of the deuteron may

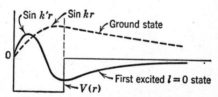

Fig. 7. Wave function of the excited state of the deuteron (if it existed).

be investigated. For $l = 0$ there are no other bound states. For in the extreme case, binding energy $W \simeq 0$, ka is still only slightly greater than $\pi/2$, since W of the ground state was already negligible compared to V_0 in equation 27a. But for the first excited state ka would have to be greater than $3\pi/2$ since the wave function ψ would have to have a radial node (Fig. 7). But from equation 33, ka is certainly less than π for all positive binding energies. Therefore, there is no bound excited state for $l = 0$. There are, of course, free states.

We shall now prove that the deuteron has no bound excited states for states of higher l. It will be assumed in this proof that the force between neutron and proton is the same for higher l as it was in the case $l = 0$. (The possibility of excited states with other total spins, especially $S = 0$, and with a different neutron-proton force will turn out to be of importance in our future discussions of neutron-proton scattering.)

To prove that no bound state exists for $l \neq 0$ we will compute the minimum well depth V just required to produce a bound state, i.e., one for which the binding energy W is just zero. This required well depth will be found to be considerably larger than the actual well depth as determined above from the binding energy in the ground state. Since the actual depth is less than the minimum required for binding for states of angular momentum $l \neq 0$ no such bound states exist.

The differential equation 26, generalized to angular momenta $l \neq 0$ becomes

$$\frac{d^2u}{dr^2} + \frac{M}{\hbar^2}(E - V)u - \frac{l(l+1)}{r^2}u = 0 \qquad (38)$$

The procedure to be followed in a general proof is as follows: Assume a square well of depth $V = -V_0$ and radius $r = a$. Find the solutions to differential equation 38 inside and outside the well. Match these solutions at $r = a$. This will give a relation between well depth V_0 and binding energy $W = -E$. Setting $W = 0$ will give the minimum well depth.

Only the proof for the case $l = 1$ will be carried out here, as an illustration. For this case, the solutions to differential equation 38 are found to be:

$$u - (\sin kr)/kr - \cos kr \qquad r < a \qquad (39a)$$

$$u = e^{-\alpha r}[(1/\alpha r) + 1] \qquad r > a \qquad (39b)$$

where
$$k^2 = M(V_0 - W)/\hbar^2 \qquad (40a)$$

$$\alpha^2 = MW/\hbar^2 \qquad (40b)$$

It will be simpler to set $W = 0$ before satisfying the boundary conditions. As $\alpha \to 0$, the outside solution (39b) becomes (except for a multiplying factor)

$$u = 1/r \qquad r \geq a \tag{41}$$

This outside solution satisfies

$$(d/dr)(ru) = 0 \qquad r \geq a \tag{42}$$

The inside solution, in order to match, must satisfy the same condition at $r = a$

$$\frac{d}{d(kr)} (kr\, u) = kr \sin kr \bigg|_{r=a}$$

$$= ka \sin ka = 0 \tag{43}$$

or

$$ka = \pi \tag{43a}$$

Using the definition of k with $W = 0$ from equation 50a:

$$MV_0 a^2/\hbar^2 = \pi^2 \tag{44}$$

This required well depth V_0 is almost four times as large as the actual well depth in the ground state (equation 32). The latter satisfied an equation like 43a, in which ka was slightly greater than $\pi/2$ but definitely less than π (equation 33).

Similar proofs with larger values of l would lead to even larger required values of ka.

IX. SCATTERING OF NEUTRONS BY FREE PROTONS

The theory of scattering developed by Born and others is presented in Mott and Massey, *Theory of Atomic Collisions* (1933). The most important result of this theory is the cross section for scattering in the center-of-mass coordinates:

$$d\sigma = \frac{2\pi \sin\theta \, d\theta}{4k^2} \left| \sum_l (2l+1) P_l(\cos\theta)(e^{2i\delta_l} - 1) \right|^2 \qquad (45)$$

The cross section $d\sigma$ is defined as the number of neutrons scattered per unit time by one proton through an angle between θ and $\theta + d\theta$, if there is a primary beam intensity of one neutron per unit area and per unit time. $d\Omega = 2\pi \sin\theta \, d\theta$ is the solid angle in center-of-mass coordinates, $l\hbar$ is the angular momentum of the system around its center of mass. The de Broglie wave number in these coordinates is given by:

$$k = 2\pi/\lambda = 1/\lambdabar = P/\hbar = \sqrt{2mE}/\hbar \qquad (46)$$

The relations between center-of-mass coordinates (c.m.) and laboratory coordinates (lab.) for two particles of equal mass are given by:

$$m = \frac{M_p M_n}{M_p + M_n} \simeq \frac{M}{2} \qquad (47)$$

$$\theta_{\text{c.m.}} = 2\theta_{\text{lab.}} \qquad (48)$$

$$E_{\text{c.m.}} = \tfrac{1}{2} E_{\text{lab.}} \qquad (49)$$

Equation 47 merely gives the reduced mass of the system in center-of-mass coordinates. Equation 49 states that only half of the neutron energy in the laboratory system is available in the center-of-mass system, the other half representing the kinetic energy of the center of mass. Equation 48 can be obtained from simple geometrical considerations.

The phase shifts δ_l are measured in radians, and their physical significance may be seen as follows: At large distances beyond the range of nuclear forces $V(r)$, equation 38 for the radial function

37

$u_l(r)$ associated with angular momentum l and angular distribution $P_l(\cos \theta)$ reduces to the equation of a free wave. The asymptotic solution $u_l(r)$ of equation 38 will therefore behave in the same manner, except for a possible shift in phase, as $v_l(r)$, the radial wave function of a *free* particle which has angular momentum l:

$$v_l(r) \sim \sin (kr - \tfrac{1}{2}l\pi) \qquad \text{(large } r) \qquad \text{(50a)}$$

$$u_l(r) \sim \sin (kr - \tfrac{1}{2}l\pi + \delta_l) \qquad \text{(large } r) \qquad \text{(50b)}$$

If all the phase shifts δ_l were zero, the total wave u obtained by adding up all the components of angular momentum l would appear at large distances to add up to the incident plane wave with no waves traveling in other directions. This result is verified if we set $\delta_l = 0$ in equation 45 for the scattering cross section.

It should also be noted that if the two waves u_l and v_l differ in phase by $\delta_l = \pi$, they are again indistinguishable, and the cross section (45) vanishes.

The actual computation of δ_l for a square-well potential will be carried out later. This calculation is based, as usual, on matching solutions inside and outside the well.

PHASE SHIFTS δ_l AS A FUNCTION OF ANGULAR MOMENTUM l

Classical Argument. If p is the momentum and b the impact parameter (classical distance of closest approach) then the angular momentum is given by:

$$|\mathbf{r} \times \mathbf{p}| = bp = l\hbar \qquad (51)$$

or
$$l = b(p/\hbar) = b/\lambdabar$$

An interaction will only take place if this closest approach distance b is smaller than the range of nuclear forces a, i.e., if

$$l < a/\lambdabar \qquad (52)$$

Thus for a given energy and definite wave length, only a finite number of l's contribute to the cross section for collision. The corresponding *quantum mechanical statement* is that for any integral value of l greater than $a/\lambdabar$ the phase shift δ_l will be negligibly small.

According to (52) $\lambdabar = a$ corresponds to the energy below which only the $l = 0$ term is of importance; this energy is

$$E_{\text{lab.}} = 2E_{\text{c.m.}} = 2\hbar^2/M\lambdabar^2 = 2\hbar^2/Ma^2$$

$$= \frac{2 \times 10^{-54}}{(1.6 \times 10^{-24})(2.8 \times 10^{-13})^2}$$

$$= 1.6 \times 10^{-5} \text{ erg} = 10 \text{ Mev} \qquad (53)$$

Quantum Mechanical Argument. The quantum mechanical argument is based on an approximate calculation of δ_l (see Nuclear Physics A, p. 119).

$$\sin \delta_l = (M/\hbar^2 k)\int_0^\infty V(r)u_l(r)v_l(r) \, dr \qquad (54)$$

The potential well is assumed to be effective only to a distance $r = a$, the range of the nuclear forces. On the other hand, in Nuclear Physics A (p. 115) the functions u_l and v_l are shown to be small unless $r > l\lambdabar$. The integral will be negligible unless these ranges overlap, i.e., $l < a/\lambdabar$, which is just the condition found by the classical argument.

SPHERICAL SYMMETRY OF SCATTERING

The result of these arguments is that δ_0 is the only important phase shift for energies up to 10 Mev. If all higher terms in equation 45 are dropped, the cross section becomes

$$d\sigma = d\Omega\lambdabar^2 \sin^2\delta_0 \qquad (55)$$

where

$$d\Omega = 2\pi \sin \theta \, d\theta = \text{the solid angle} \qquad (55a)$$

Thus the cross section (55) is found to be independent of direction, or spherically symmetric for neutrons below 10 Mev. This conclusion is based chiefly on the short-range nature of the forces. Thus, if spherical symmetry is found experimentally, this will verify that the forces are short range, and test the applicability of quantum mechanics to such scattering problems.

The best experimental determination of the angular distribution of scattered neutrons is based on measuring the energy distribution of the recoil protons. An elementary consideration shows that uniform angular distribution corresponds to uniform distribution in energy of the recoil protons from zero to the incident neutron energy (in the laboratory system).

Early cloud-chamber measurements of the angular distribution showed preferential neutron scattering in the forward direction, i.e., most of the recoil protons were at large angles to the beam. The energy of the protons is smaller if they are emitted at large angles. Now it could be shown that high energy tracks were often missed in the experiments because they were long enough to leave the chamber except when they were almost in the plane of the chamber. A check on the azimuthal distribution, for which there can be no asymmetry, verified this by revealing that most of the measured long tracks were in the plane of the chamber. Careful cloud-chamber experiments by Dee and Gilbert produced an exactly spherical symmetry.

Measurements of proton recoil energy by ionization chamber methods by Ladenburg and his co-workers gave an almost uniform distribution in energy. Experiments at Los Alamos by Staub and others indicate uniformity even more accurately to within an experimental error of about 1 per cent.

One of the problems for further experimental work is to measure the deviations from spherical symmetry at higher energies. (See also Chapter XIV.)

TOTAL CROSS SECTION

The total cross section for scattering of neutrons by protons follows from integration of equation 55:

$$\sigma = 4\pi \,\lambdabar^2 \sin{}^2\delta_0 \tag{56}$$

for energies of the incident neutrons less than 10 Mev, where $2\pi\lambdabar$ is the de Broglie wave length of the neutron in the center-of-mass system, and δ_0 is the phase shift of the scattered wave function for $l = 0$. Outside the range of the nuclear forces, the wave function, u (a solution of equation 38 with $l = 0$ and E positive), will be proportional to $\sin{}(kr + \delta_0)$, where $k = \sqrt{ME}/\hbar$ (E = neutron energy in the center-of-mass system = $\frac{1}{2}E_{\text{lab.}}$; M = mass of neutron).

The phase shift δ_0 is determined from the condition that the logarithmic derivative of the wave function must be continuous at the boundary of the nuclear forces, $r = a$. For the outside wave function this derivative is:

$$d/dr \; (\log u)\Big|_{a+} = k \cot (ka + \delta_0) \qquad (57)$$

The logarithmic derivative of the inside wave function can be calculated for any given energy from the nuclear potential. However, it is most desirable to make the calculation as free as possible from the details of the potential function used. This can be done because it can be shown that, independently of the shape and the range of the potential, and independently of the energy of the neutrons (up to about 10 Mev), the logarithmic derivative of the inside function has the same value as for the ground state, viz.,

$$d/dr \; (\log u)\Big|_{a-} = -\alpha \qquad (58)$$

To prove this, we write the wave equations for the two states: Ground state:

$$d^2 u_0/dr^2 + (M/\hbar^2)[-W - V(r)]u_0 = 0 \qquad (59)$$

State of energy E:

$$d^2 u/dr^2 + (M/\hbar^2)[E - V(r)]u = 0 \qquad (60)$$

Multiplying the first by u, the second by u_0, subtracting, and integrating from 0 to r_1 gives

$$\left[u \frac{du_0}{dr} - u_0 \frac{du}{dr} \right]_0^{r_1} - \frac{M}{\hbar^2} (E + W) \int_0^{r_1} uu_0 \, dr = 0 \qquad (61)$$

Since $u(0) = u_0(0) = 0$, dividing by $u(a)u_0(a)$ and setting $r_1 = a$ gives

$$\left(\frac{du_0/dr}{u_0} - \frac{du/dr}{u} \right)_a = \left(\frac{d \log u_0}{dr} - \frac{d \log u}{dr} \right)_a$$

$$= \frac{M}{\hbar^2} (E + W) \frac{\int_0^a uu_0 \, dr}{u(a)u_0(a)} \qquad (62)$$

Now $\int_0^a uu_0 \, dr = a(uu_0)_{\max}.\xi$, where $0 < \xi < 1$, and since the maximum value of uu_0 is not much larger than the value at a (this follows, e.g., from Fig. 6),

$$\int_0^a u_0 u \, dr = \gamma a u_0(a) u(a), \quad 0 < \gamma < 1 \tag{63}$$

For the rectangular-well potential an approximate calculation gives $\gamma = \frac{1}{2}$. Inserting $(d \log u_0/dr)_a = -\alpha$, we get:

$$(d \log u/dr)_a = -\alpha - (ME/\hbar^2 + MW/\hbar^2)\gamma a$$
$$= -\alpha - (k^2 + \alpha^2)\gamma a \tag{64}$$

Thus the equation for δ_0 is

$$k \cot(ka + \delta_0) = -\alpha - (\alpha^2 + k^2)(\gamma a) \tag{65}$$

A first approximation to the correct solution of this equation neglects the second term on the right and the term ka in the cotangent. This is equivalent to setting the range, a, of the nuclear forces equal to zero. Then we get

$$\cot(\delta_0) = -\alpha/k \tag{66}$$

Setting $ka = 0$ is not a bad approximation for neutrons with wave lengths greater than a few times a, i.e., with energies less than a few Mev. The neglect of the last term $(\alpha^2 + k^2)\gamma a$, compared to α, involves an error of the same order as that of ka; but it should be remembered that for the actual range of the forces $(a \sim 3 \times 10^{-13}$ cm$)$, the product αa is not very small but has a value of about $\frac{1}{2}$.

Substituting (66) into (56) we get

$$\sin^2\delta_0 = \frac{1}{1 + \cot^2\delta_0} = \frac{k^2}{k^2 + \alpha^2} \tag{67}$$

and

$$\sigma = \frac{4\pi}{k^2}\sin^2\delta_0 = \frac{4\pi}{\alpha^2 + k^2} = \frac{4\pi\hbar^2}{M}\frac{1}{E + W} \tag{68}$$

The next approximation (see Nuclear Physics A, p. 119) takes account of $a \neq 0$ and leads, for the rectangular-well potential, to an additional factor $1 + \alpha a$ in the cross section.

EXPERIMENTAL RESULTS ON NEUTRON-PROTON SCATTERING

The first experiments on neutron-proton scattering used 2.5-Mev D-D neutrons. The cross section measured was within 20 to 30 per cent of the theoretical value which was then within experimental error. However, the cross section was then also measured for *thermal neutrons* (very slow) for which equation 68 gives

$$\sigma \simeq 2.4 \text{ barns} \quad (1 \text{ barn} = 10^{-24} \text{ cm}^2) \tag{69}$$

The experimental result was ~50 barns.

Two reasons for this discrepancy are:

1. The finite range, a, of the nuclear forces required the correction factor $(1 + \alpha a)$ as mentioned. When this was included, the theoretical cross section rose to 3.8 barns.

2. Fermi showed that protons bound in molecules should have a σ larger than that for free protons by a factor of about 2.5. This second correction brings the experimental value for free protons down to ~20 barns. This was checked by measuring the scattering at neutron energies between 1 and 10 ev, where the molecular binding would presumably have no effect. The measured value at 10 ev was 21 barns, still a long way from 3.8 barns.

SINGLET STATE OF THE DEUTERON

In 1935 Wigner made a suggestion which closed the gap. He pointed out that the ground state of the deuteron gives information about the interaction of neutrons and protons only if their spins are parallel, and that there must also be a state of the deuteron in which the spins of neutron and proton are antiparallel (singlet state). We are still free to make assumptions about this singlet state, and a small energy W for this state would lead to a large scattering cross section at low neutron energy E, since σ is proportional to $1/(W + E)$. Since W is not known it must be deduced from the observed cross section. Writing

σ_s = scattering cross section due to singlet state; spins antiparallel

σ_t = scattering cross section due to triplet state; spins parallel

σ = total scattering cross section, we get

$$\sigma = \tfrac{1}{4}\sigma_s + \tfrac{3}{4}\sigma_t \tag{70}$$

The $\tfrac{1}{4}$ and $\tfrac{3}{4}$ are the statistical weights of the singlet state and the triplet state, respectively.

To prove that these are the correct statistical weights, it is necessary only to construct the sets of wave functions of the two particles (1) and (2) corresponding to the two situations. Let α

be the eigenstate of spin $+\frac{1}{2}$ and β of spin $-\frac{1}{2}$ along some fixed z axis for a single particle. Then for two particles, 1 and 2,

$$\alpha(1)\alpha(2) \text{ has } M = +1$$

($M = z$ component of total spin)

$$\beta(1)\beta(2) \text{ has } M = -1$$

$$[\alpha(1)\beta(2) + \alpha(2)\beta(1)]/\sqrt{2} \text{ has } M = 0$$

$$[\alpha(1)\beta(2) - \alpha(2)\beta(1)]/\sqrt{2} \text{ has } M = 0 \quad \text{~~has~~}M=\text{~~?~~}$$

The first three functions have total spin 1; the last has total spin 0; there are no more linearly independent functions. Therefore, the statistical weights 3 and 1 are justified.

Inserting the weights from equation 70, and denoting the energies of triplet and singlet state by W_t and W_s, respectively, equation 68 for the cross section becomes

$$\sigma = \frac{\pi\hbar^2}{M}\left(\frac{3}{E + W_t} + \frac{1}{E + |W_s|}\right) \tag{71}$$

Inserting the measured σ, and $W_t = 2.19$ Mev, it is deduced that $|W_s| = 0.064$ Mev, very much smaller than W_t.

One test of Wigner's hypothesis is by measurement of the cross section over the range 0 to about 5 Mev, where the theoretical

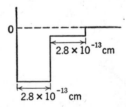

FIG. 8. Potential well of the deuteron giving the best fit to scattering experiments.

expression for σ should hold. This is not an easy measurement. It was done very carefully by Williams and collaborators [*] at Minnesota and Los Alamos. The calculations were carried out by Bohm and Richman. With a rectangular potential hole of width $a = 2.8 \times 10^{-13}$ cm and depth adjusted to give the binding

* Bailey, Bennett, Bergstralh, Nuckolls, Richards, and Williams, Phys. Rev. 70, 583 (1946); for lower energies D. H. Frisch, Phys. Rev. 70, 589 (1946).

energy of the deuteron and the scattering cross section at very low
energy, there was complete agreement save at the upper end near
5 Mev.   There better agreement was achieved with a potential
of the form indicated in Fig. 8, i.e., a deep narrow' well, plus a
shallow well of double width.

Evidence for Neutron Spin.   These experiments are also strong
evidence that the neutron spin is exactly $\frac{1}{2}$.   If it were $\frac{3}{2}$, there
would be two states of the deuteron contributing to the scattering:
a quintet, $S = 2$, with statistical weight 5, and a triplet, $S = 1$,
with statistical weight 3.   This would give

$$\sigma = \frac{\pi\hbar^2}{2M}\left(\frac{3}{E + W_t} + \frac{5}{E + W_q}\right) \tag{72}$$

If this is made to agree with the measured σ at low energies by a
choice of W_q, then it gives results for $2E \sim 400$ to 800 kev, which
are too large by a factor greater than 1.5, far outside the experimental error.   For spin of the neutron greater than $\frac{3}{2}$, one must
use $l \neq 0$ in order to get the right total spin for the ground state
of the deuteron.   As was pointed out in Chapter VIII, $l \neq 0$ is
very unlikely on general principles.

Sign of Energy in Singlet State.   The measurement of the cross
section does not give information as to whether the singlet state
is bound or virtual (only $\beta^2 = M|W_s|/\hbar^2$ occurs in the cross sec-
tion; see equation 68).   All evidence favors its being virtual.   The
most important evidence is the scattering of neutrons in ortho-
and para-hydrogen (Chapter X), which also constitutes a good

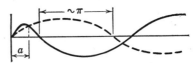

FIG. 9a.   Wave function of the
singlet state of the deuteron
(virtual).

FIG. 9b.   Wave function of the triplet
state for low neutron energy.   (Bro-
ken line: free particle.)

check on Wigner's hypothesis that the scattering depends strongly
on spin.

Assuming that the singlet state is virtual, its wave function will
look like Fig. 9a, for large λ, i.e., slow neturons, because the phase
shift δ_0 approaches zero.   On the other hand, for the triplet state,
as $E \to 0$, δ_0 goes to π (see equation 66) and the wave function will

have the shape of Fig. 9b. In either case the scattered amplitude of the neutron is proportional to $e^{2i\delta_0} - 1$. Therefore, for low energies, the scattered amplitude is:

For the triplet state, setting

$$\delta_0 = \pi - \delta', \text{ with } \delta' \text{ small,}$$

$$e^{2i\delta_0} - 1 = -2i\delta' \tag{73}$$

For the singlet state (assumed virtual):

$$e^{2i\delta_0} - 1 = 2i\delta_0 \tag{74}$$

triplet

Thus for small energies, the scattered amplitudes have opposite signs for real and virtual states ($\delta' > 0$ since $\pi/2 < \delta_0 < \pi$).

Assuming a virtual singlet state, the singlet scattering cross section should be corrected for finite range by a factor $(1 - \beta a)$, where $\beta = \sqrt{M|W_s|}/\hbar$.

X. SCATTERING OF NEUTRONS BY PROTONS BOUND IN MOLECULES

The scattering of neutrons by free protons has been discussed in the last chapter. It is now worth while to investigate the effects of binding of the proton in molecules.

THREE EFFECTS OF BINDING OF PROTON IN MOLECULES

1. *Chemical Bond Effect.* If it is assumed that the scattering may be treated in Born's approximation, then the differential cross section is

$$d\sigma = \text{constant} \times m^2 \times \left| \int \psi_1{}^* V \psi_2 \right|^2 d\Omega \qquad (75)$$

where m is the reduced mass of scattered particle and scatterer, and V is their interaction potential. The quantity within the absolute value signs is the matrix element of V between the initial and the final states. Equation 75 comes from treating as a perturbation the term $(2m/\hbar^2)V$ in the Schrödinger equation

$$\nabla^2 \psi + (2m/\hbar^2)(E - V)\psi = 0 \qquad (76)$$

Solution of the problem gives the cross section proportional to the square of the matrix element of the perturbation which leads to equation 75.

Now the reduced mass m depends on whether the proton is free or fixed. (The integral in equation 75 does not.) The two limiting cases are:

1. Proton free: $m = \frac{1}{2}M$.
2. Proton bound to *heavy* molecule (e.g., paraffin): $m = M$. We therefore expect

$$\sigma \text{ (bound)} = 4\sigma \text{ (free)} \qquad (77)$$

In order to use this argument it is necessary to:
(1) be able to say when a proton is free and when bound, and
(2) justify the use of Born's approximation.

Fermi (as reported in Nuclear Physics B, p. 122) examined the first of these problems and showed that essentially the proton is bound if

$$E_n \ll h\nu(\approx 0.4 \text{ ev for CH bond in paraffin}) \qquad (78)$$

where E_n is the neutron energy and ν is the frequency of vibration of the proton in the subgroup of the molecule. Figure 10 shows the ratio of the actual to the free cross section as a function of E_n

For $E_n < h\nu$, the neutron cannot lose energy to the vibration at $E_n = h\nu$ the abrupt rise in the cross section comes from a contribution due to the possibility of losing one quantum of energy to the vibration. Similar breaks occur at $E_n = 2h\nu$, etc. For E_n much larger than the vibration energy of the proton in the molecule, the proton is easily dislodged from its position and acts as a free proton: $\sigma \rightarrow \sigma$ (free).

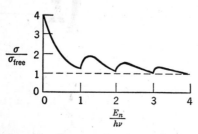

FIG. 10.   Cross section for scattering of neutrons by elastically bound protons.

Neutrons with $E_n < h\nu$ will be more difficult to slow down than those with $E_n > h\nu$, because they cannot lose energy to the vibration of the *proton* in the subgroup of the molecule. They can, however, lose energy to vibrations of whole CH_2 subgroups, which have smaller quantum energies. Speaking practically, it can be said that neutrons are easily "cooled" to room temperature ($\frac{1}{40}$ ev), but are with difficulty "cooled" to 20° K or lower.

Of course, Born's approximation is not directly justifiable for neutrons with E_n of the order of 1 ev, as the perturbation (which is considered "small") is of the order of 10 Mev (interaction potential of neutron and proton). However, it has been shown (Nuclear Physics B, p. 123) that it is possible to construct an artificial interaction potential which would give physically the same scattering and yet satisfy the conditions for Born's approximation. The magnitude of the artificial potential is chosen small enough to justify Born's approximation, and the range is increased to maintain the same scattering. This is justifiable because the wave function of the proton in the molecule occupies a much larger region of space than both the true and the artificial potentials. The results quoted hold using this artificial potential.

2. *Molecular Velocity Effect.* When the neutron energy is of the order of thermal energies or smaller, it is certainly not permissible to neglect the thermal motion of the proton. Consider a neutron with velocity $\mathbf{v}$ which passes through a thickness L of scattering material, and consider collisions with protons which are moving with velocity $\mathbf{u}$. Then the cross section σ_1 is a function of $|\mathbf{v} - \mathbf{u}|$ and the number of collisions per second is proportional to $\sigma_1 \times |\mathbf{v} - \mathbf{u}|$. The number of collisions in the scatterer will then be proportional to $(L/v)\sigma_1|\mathbf{v} - \mathbf{u}|$. The effective scattering cross section, defined as proportional to the number of collisions per unit thickness of the scatterer, is

$$\sigma_{\text{eff.}}(\mathbf{u}) = [\sigma_1(\mathbf{v} - \mathbf{u})] \times |\mathbf{v} - \mathbf{u}|/v \qquad (79)$$

To obtain the actual effective cross section this expression must be averaged over the distribution in $\mathbf{u}$ (for the case when σ_1 is independent of the magnitude and the direction of $(\mathbf{v} - \mathbf{u})$ see Schwinger, Phys. Rev. **58**, 1004).

3. *Scattering of Neutrons by Ortho- and Para-Hydrogen.* An experimental comparison of the scattering from ortho- and from para-hydrogen was first suggested by Teller in 1936 to test the spin dependence of the neutron-proton interaction. An ortho-hydrogen molecule has a total proton spin of 1, whereas a para-hydrogen molecule has a total proton spin of 0. Thus ortho-hydrogen has a wave function symmetric in the proton spins and has a statistical weight of three, whereas para-hydrogen has an antisymmetric nuclear spin function and a statistical weight of one. Since protons obey Fermi statistics, the total molecular wave function *

$$\psi = \psi \text{ (electronic)} \cdot \psi \text{ (nuclear spin)} \cdot \psi \text{ (rotation)} \qquad (80)$$

must change sign on interchanging positions and spins of the protons (cf. Chapter V). For H_2, it is known from molecular theory that this interchange of protons does not change the sign of ψ(electronic). Therefore ψ(rotation) must be symmetric when ψ(nuclear spin) is antisymmetric, and vice versa. Consequently, ortho-hydrogen can have only odd rotational quantum numbers $(j = 1, 3, \cdots)$ and para-hydrogen can have only even rotational quantum numbers $(j = 0, 2, \cdots)$. The lowest energy level

* The vibrational part has been left out in 80 because it is always symmetric in the two protons.

$(j = 0)$ is therefore in para-hydrogen. The rotational energy is proportional to $j(j + 1)/2I$, where I = the moment of inertia. Because of the statistical weights, there is three times as much ortho- as para-hydrogen in an equilibrium mixture at ordinary temperatures.

Normally, there is practically no conversion between ortho- and para-hydrogen because the spin of one proton must be turned over for this purpose, and the forces acting on the proton spin (magnetic forces) are extremely small. Thus a 3-to-1 mixture can be preserved at low temperature. However, in the presence of a suitable catalyst conversion can occur; then at very low temperatures practically all of the molecules go to the lowest energy state—the para $j = 0$ form. Comparing experiments on the separated para-form with those on the quenched 3-to-1 mixture will give also the results for ortho-hydrogen alone.

We shall now derive an expression for the scattered intensity from a molecule of ortho- or para-hydrogen when the incident neutron energy is so small that λ_n is much greater than the distance between the atoms in the H_2 molecule ≈ 0.75 angstrom unit. This is true for neutrons at temperatures of $20°$ K or lower. The derivation follows that of Schwinger and Teller (Phys. Rev. **52**, 286, 1937).

Let the Pauli spin operators of neutron and proton be σ_N and σ_P. (These are twice the spin operators $\mathbf{S}_N$ and $\mathbf{S}_P$ in units of $\hbar$.) We wish to investigate the eigenvalues of the operator $\sigma_N \cdot \sigma_P$. Let $\mathbf{S}$ be the total nuclear spin of the neutron and the proton

$$\mathbf{S} = \mathbf{S}_N + \mathbf{S}_P \tag{81}$$

Therefore

$$\mathbf{S}^2 = \mathbf{S}_N{}^2 + \mathbf{S}_P{}^2 + 2\mathbf{S}_N \cdot \mathbf{S}_P \tag{82}$$

since $\mathbf{S}_N$ and $\mathbf{S}_P$ commute.

Now we already know that $\mathbf{S}^2$, $\mathbf{S}_N{}^2$, and $\mathbf{S}_P{}^2$ are constants of motion and we know their eigenvalues: $S(S + 1)$, $S_N(S_N + 1)$, and $S_P(S_P + 1)$, respectively, where S is 0 and 1 for the singlet and the triplet states of the deuteron, respectively, and S_N and S_P are each $\frac{1}{2}$. Equation 82 can therefore be used to determine

$$\mathbf{S}_N \cdot \mathbf{S}_P = \frac{1}{2}[S(S + 1) - S_N(S_N + 1) - S_P(S_P + 1)]$$

$$= S(S + 1)/2 - \frac{3}{4}$$

and therefore

$$\boldsymbol{\sigma}_N \cdot \boldsymbol{\sigma}_P = 2S(S+1) - 3$$
$$= 1 \text{ for } S = 1 \text{ (triplet)} \tag{83}$$
$$= -3 \text{ for } S = 0 \text{ (singlet)}$$

Now let a_0 be the amplitude of the scattered neutron wave in the singlet state (for the scattering by a free proton) and let a_1 be the corresponding triplet amplitude, so that

$$\sigma_s = 4\pi a_0{}^2, \quad \sigma_t = 4\pi a_1{}^2, \quad \sigma = \tfrac{1}{4}\sigma_s + \tfrac{3}{4}\sigma_t = \pi a_0{}^2 + 3\pi a_1{}^2 \tag{84}$$

Then the formula

$$\text{scattered amplitude} = \frac{a_0 + 3a_1}{4} + \frac{a_1 - a_0}{4} \boldsymbol{\sigma}_N \cdot \boldsymbol{\sigma}_P \tag{85}$$

is easily seen to be correct for both triplet and singlet states, by direct substitution from equation 83.

Since the distance between protons in the molecule is assumed to be much smaller than $\lambdabar_n$, it is permissible to neglect the small phase difference in the scattering from the two protons and add amplitudes directly. Therefore the scattered amplitude from a molecule of H_2 is

$$A = \frac{a_0 + 3a_1}{2} + \frac{a_1 - a_0}{4} \boldsymbol{\sigma}_N \cdot (\boldsymbol{\sigma}_{P_1} + \boldsymbol{\sigma}_{P_2})$$

$$= \frac{a_0 + 3a_1}{2} + \frac{a_1 - a_0}{2} \boldsymbol{\sigma}_N \cdot \mathbf{S}_H \tag{86}$$

where P_1 and P_2 denote the two protons and $\tfrac{1}{2}(\boldsymbol{\sigma}_{P_1} + \boldsymbol{\sigma}_{P_2}) = \mathbf{S}_H$ is the total spin of the two protons in the H_2 molecule. The scattered intensity (or differential cross section) is then

$$A^2 = \tfrac{1}{4}(a_0 + 3a_1)^2 + \tfrac{1}{2}(a_0 + 3a_1)(a_1 - a_0) \boldsymbol{\sigma}_N \cdot \mathbf{S}_H$$
$$+ \tfrac{1}{4}(a_1 - a_0)^2 (\boldsymbol{\sigma}_N \cdot \mathbf{S}_H)^2 \tag{87}$$

for a beam of neutrons with spin $\boldsymbol{\sigma}_N$. This must be averaged over all polarizations of the beam. The average of $\boldsymbol{\sigma}_N \cdot \mathbf{S}_H$ is zero. Furthermore, writing the scalar product out in Cartesian components,

$$(\boldsymbol{\sigma}_N \cdot \mathbf{S}_H)^2 = \sigma_{Nx}{}^2 S_{Hx}{}^2 + \cdots + \sigma_{Nx}\sigma_{Ny} S_{Hx} S_{Hy} + \cdots,$$

the average of $\sigma_{Nx}\sigma_{Ny}$ is zero and $\sigma_{Nx}{}^2 = \sigma_{Ny}{}^2 = \sigma_{Nz}{}^2 = 1$. Therefore, on averaging

$$(\sigma_N \cdot \mathbf{S}_H)^2 = S_{Hx}{}^2 + S_{Hy}{}^2 + S_{Hz}{}^2 = \mathbf{S}_H{}^2 = S_H(S_H + 1)$$

With these results, the differential cross-section becomes

$$d\sigma = \tfrac{1}{4}[(a_0 + 3a_1)^2 + (a_1 - a_0)^2 S_H(S_H + 1)]\, d\Omega \quad (88)$$

Unless $a_1 = a_0$, there is more scattering from ortho- than from para-hydrogen. Since all the experiments indicate that there is more ortho scattering than para scattering, $a_1 \neq a_0$; *this proves Wigner's hypothesis that the neutron-proton force is spin dependent.*

It was shown in the previous chapter that if the singlet state of the deuteron is virtual, a_1 and a_0 have opposite sign, and vice versa. Now $a_1{}^2 = \sigma_t/4\pi$ can be deduced from the binding energy of the deuteron, and $a_0{}^2 = \sigma_s/4\pi$ can then be determined from the scattering of slow neutrons by free protons (see Chapter IX). The results are $a_0{}^2 \approx 18/\pi$ barns, $3a_1{}^2 \approx 3/\pi$ barns. So $|a_1| \approx 1/\sqrt{\pi}$, $|a_0| \approx 4.2/\sqrt{\pi}$; this gives no check on relative sign of a_0 and a_1. But, because of the form of equation 88, opposite signs of a_0 and a_1 will give a much larger ratio of the ortho to the para cross sections than the same signs. In fact, if a_1 and a_0 have the same sign, the values of $|a_1|$ and $|a_0|$ just quoted give by equation 88 about 1.4 for the ratio of the ortho cross section to the para cross section, whereas if a_1 and a_0 have opposite signs the ratio is about 35. This great difference is easily checked by experiment. All experiments indicate that the signs of a_0 and a_1 are opposite; therefore, *the singlet state is a virtual state.*

COMPARISON WITH EXPERIMENT

Before comparison of equation 88 with experiment, corrections must be made for the chemical bond effect, the molecular motion effect, and the slight phase shift because the scattering protons are a finite though small fraction of a wave length apart.

According to the chemical bond effect, the cross section for low-energy neutron scattering is proportional to the square of the reduced mass of the system. Since this reduced mass is $\frac{2}{3}M$ for a neutron and a hydrogen molecule, whereas it is $\frac{1}{2}M$ for a neutron and a proton, the result given by equation 88 must be increased by a factor $\frac{16}{9}$.

The molecular velocity effect which takes into account the change in effective number of collisions produced by the relative neutron-molecule velocity was given in equation 79. Evaluation for H_2 gas at 20° K, and for neutrons of a kinetic energy corresponding to kT at 20° K, gives a correction factor of 1.247.

The phase shift effect decreases the results by about 7 to 10 per cent. Taking the entire solid angle of 4π, the formulas to be compared with experiments are:

$$\sigma_{\text{para}} = 6.47(3a_1 + a_0)^2 \tag{89}$$

$$\sigma_{\text{ortho}} = 6.29[(3a_1 + a_0)^2 + 2(a_0 - a_1)^2] + 1.45(a_0 - a_1)^2 \tag{90}$$

together with the free proton cross section (equation 84). The last term in σ_{ortho} was added to take into account inelastic scattering by conversion of ortho to para. This process is energetically possible but its cross section is small.

Experiments were made first by Brickwedde, Dunning, and others (Phys. Rev. **54**, 266, 1938), and later by Alvarez and Pitzer (Phys. Rev. **58**, 1003, 1940) using a neutron velocity selector. In 1946 the experiment was repeated with improved technique by DeWire, Sutton, and others at the Los Alamos Laboratory. The results of the two last experiments are:

	Alvarez and Pitzer	Los Alamos
σ_{para}	5.2	4.0
σ_{ortho}	100	125

The ortho and para cross sections together are sufficient to determine a_0 and a_1. This was done by Schwinger and Hamermesh for the experiments of Alvarez and Pitzer. The result was a very small value for a_1. From a_1 it is possible to derive the range of the nuclear forces using the theory developed in Chapters IX and X which gives the approximate result

$$a_1 = 1/\alpha + \tfrac{1}{2}a \tag{91}$$

When the observed a_1 was inserted into equation 91, the result was 0 or a slightly negative value for the range of the nuclear forces, a. This result was clearly unacceptable.

The same evaluation applied to the Los Alamos results gives a much more reasonable value for the range. The improvement is mostly attributable to the increase of the ortho-scattering cross section. It was observed in the Los Alamos experiments that some conversion of ortho- into para-hydrogen was constantly taking place. At frequent intervals the composition of the hydrogen was therefore determined. It is believed that the low value reported by Alvarez and Pitzer might have been due to an unexpectedly low content of ortho-hydrogen in their scatterer.

Probably the most accurate evaluation is based on the use of the scattering cross section of free protons together with the para cross section, using equations 84 and 89. This procedure with the Los Alamos experiments leads to a range of the forces in the triplet state of

$$a = 1.8 \times 10^{-13} \text{ cm} \tag{92}$$

This range is considerably smaller than the usually assumed value of 2.8×10^{-13} cm, which is derived from the rather accurate experiments on the scattering of protons by protons. If the nuclear forces are the same for protons and neutrons, for which there is good reason (see Chapter XII), then the range of the proton-proton scattering must also be valid in the singlet state of proton-neutron scattering. However, it is very well possible that the range in the triplet state is different, and there may even be some slight indications from the meson theory of nuclear forces that the triplet range should be smaller. Although the scattering experiments are not yet as precise as would be desirable, it still seems that the difference between the two ranges is outside the experimental error.

The results from ortho- and para-hydrogen scattering justify these definite conclusions:

1. The neutron-proton force is spin dependent. This follows from the definite experimental fact that the ortho and para cross sections are different, which implies $a_1 \neq a_0$ and the spin dependence of the forces.

2. The singlet state of the deuteron is virtual. This follows from the fact that the singlet scattering amplitude a_0 must have

opposite (and therefore positive) sign from that of a_1 in order to give a large ratio of ortho to para scattering, as observed.

3. The spin of the neutron is $\frac{1}{2}$. This follows again from the fairly large observed ratio of ortho to para cross sections, viz.,

$$\frac{\sigma_{\text{ortho}}}{\sigma_{\text{para}}} \simeq 30$$

A spin of $S_N = \frac{3}{2}$ or higher would require a much smaller ratio, say 2, or less. To see this, we rewrite the scattering amplitude for a free proton (equation 85) for $S_N = \frac{3}{2}$:

$$(3a_1 + 5a_2)/8 + (a_2 - a_1)\,\sigma_N \cdot \sigma_P/8 \tag{93}$$

The scattering by a hydrogen molecule (88) is then changed to:

$$\sigma/4\pi = (3a_1 + 5a_2)^2/16 + (a_2 - a_1)^2 S(S + 1)/16 \tag{94}$$

where $S = 0$ for para, 1 for ortho as before.

Since the coefficients in the first term are now different from before, there is no longer near-cancellation of the a_1 and the a_2 term, even if the quintuplet state is virtual. Indeed, a_2 must be considerably larger (about twice) than a_1 to explain the scattering of slow neutrons by protons, and, moreover, a_2 has the larger coefficient. An additional reason is that the second term in equation 94 has a relatively smaller numerical coefficient.

Thus a spin of $S_N = \frac{3}{2}$ is ruled out. Higher values of the neutron spin would be inconsistent with the deuteron spin of 1 and the proton spin of $\frac{1}{2}$.

4. The range of the nuclear forces in the triplet state seems to be significantly smaller than in the singlet state, namely, 1.8×10^{-13} cm in the triplet as compared with 2.8×10^{-13} cm in the singlet. However, this conclusion may be in conflict with the accurate measurements of the cross section at higher neutron energies.

XI. INTERACTION OF THE DEUTERON WITH RADIATION

PHOTODISINTEGRATION

Photodisintegration has been used to obtain the binding energy of the deuteron (Chapter VIII). It will now be discussed from the point of view of its cross section. The discussion is restricted to low energies (several Mev) so that all the needed constants can be obtained from deuteron binding energy and neutron-proton scattering results. Furthermore, at these energies, the transition probability is attributable almost entirely to the dipole (electric and magnetic) moment. Quadrupole and higher multipole transitions would be important at high energies (100 Mev).

The cross section for γ-ray absorption is (compare Heitler, *Quantum Theory of Radiation*, pp. 121, 122)

$$\sigma = 2 \frac{\omega m^2 v}{\hbar^3 c} |M|^2 \tag{95}$$

where $\omega = 2\pi\nu$ is the (circular) frequency of the incoming photon, m is the reduced mass of the system $= \frac{1}{2}M$, and v is the velocity of the emitted particle. M is the matrix element, for the transition, of the electric or magnetic dipole moment.

Electric Interaction. We first discuss the effect due to *electric* interaction. Since the z-component of the electric dipole moment of the proton in the center-of-mass system is $ez/2$, if z is the coordinate of the proton relative to the neutron, we have

$$M_{\text{el.}} = (e/2) \int \psi_i z \, \psi_f \, d\tau \tag{96}$$

where ψ_i is the wave function of the deuteron in the ground state. This was shown to be equal to

$$\psi_i = \sqrt{\alpha/2\pi} \, e^{-ar} \, (1 + \frac{1}{2}\alpha a) \tag{97}$$

over most of space.

The final state must be a p-state to produce a non-vanishing matrix element. Since no stable p-states exist (Chapter VIII), it must be a p-state of the continuous spectrum. For energies small compared to the well depth, the wave function of the p-state will be practically zero inside the well. Thus the potential energy of the p-state will be small, and the state will be only very slightly distorted from that of a p-state with no potential well. In the calculation of the matrix element, therefore, the wave function of a free particle of angular momentum 1 may be used for ψ_f. If this is inserted into equations 96 and 95, the result is

$$d\sigma = 2(e^2/\hbar c) \cos^2 \chi [\alpha k^3/(\alpha^2 + k^2)^3] \, d\Omega (1 + \alpha a) \qquad (98)$$

where k is the wave number of the system after absorption of the quantum, so that:

$$\left. \begin{array}{l} E \text{ of system} = h\nu - W_1 = \hbar^2 k^2/M \\[2mm] \text{Deuteron binding energy} = W_1 = \hbar^2 \alpha^2/M \end{array} \right\} \qquad (99)$$

χ is the angle between the direction of *polarization* of the γ-ray and the direction of motion of the proton. The factor $\cos^2 \chi$ arises from the wave function of the final state. If the beam is unpolarized, and we average over all directions of polarization

$$\overline{\cos^2 \chi} = \tfrac{1}{2} \sin^2 \theta \qquad (100)$$

when θ is the angle of the emitted proton with the direction of *propagation* of the incident photon. On the other hand, if we hold the direction of polarization fixed and average over all proton directions, we get

$$\int \cos^2 \chi \, d\Omega = 4\pi/3 \qquad (101)$$

Using equations 98, 99, and 101, the total cross section becomes

$$\sigma_{\text{el.}} = \frac{8\pi}{3} \frac{e^2}{\hbar c} \frac{\hbar^2}{M} \frac{W_1^{1/2} E^{3/2}}{(E + W_1)^3} (1 + \alpha a) \qquad (102)$$

where the factor $(1 + \alpha a)$ arises from the normalization of the ground-state wave function (equation 97).

The *photomagnetic disintegration* makes use of the magnetic dipole moment. If μ_p and μ_N are the moments of proton and neutron, respectively, in units of the nuclear magneton, then the magnetic dipole moment of the system is

$$(e\hbar/2Mc)(\mu_p \sigma_p + \mu_N \sigma_N) \qquad (103)$$

The initial state is, as before, the $^3S_1$ ground state of the deuteron the spatial dependence of which is given approximately by equation 97. The final state must also be an S-state, or the integration over angles will vanish. However, all excited ^3S-states are orthogonal to the ground state since they are produced by the same potential well. The only possibility, therefore, is that the final state be the virtual $^1S_0$ state. Since this final state is an S-state the emitted protons will show isotropic distribution in angle, in contrast with the result (equation 98) for photoelectric disintegration in which the final state was a P-state.

The matrix element for the transition is therefore given by:

$$M_m = (e\hbar/2Mc) \sum_{\text{spin}} \chi_0 \, (\mu_p\boldsymbol{\sigma}_p + \mu_N\boldsymbol{\sigma}_N)\chi_1 \int \psi_i\psi_f \, d\tau \qquad (104)$$

where χ_1 and χ_0 are the spin functions of the triplet and the singlet states, and ψ_i is the wave function for the ground state which is approximated by equation 97. ψ_f is the wave function for the singlet S-state in the continuous spectrum, and is normalized per unit energy interval.

If the matrix element (104) is computed and substituted into formula 95 for the cross section, the result is:

$$\sigma_m = \frac{2\pi}{3} \frac{e^2}{\hbar c} \frac{\hbar^2}{M} \frac{\sqrt{W_1}\sqrt{E}(\sqrt{W_1} + \sqrt{W_0})^2}{(E + W_1)(E + W_0)Mc^2} (\mu_p - \mu_N)^2 \quad (105)$$

where E and W_1 are defined as in the case for photoelectric disintegration (equation 99): $E = h\nu - W_1$, $W_1 =$ deuteron binding energy. W_0 is the fictitious binding energy for the singlet state the numerical value of which is determined from the low-energy, singlet-scattering cross section

$$\sigma_0 = 4\pi a_0{}^2 = 4\pi(1 - \beta a)/(\beta^2 + k^2)$$
$$= 4\pi\hbar^2(1 - \beta a)/M(W_0 + E) \qquad (106)$$

The factor $(\mu_p - \mu_N)^2$ in equation 105 can be understood if we write the operator $\mu_p\boldsymbol{\sigma}_p + \mu_N\boldsymbol{\sigma}_N$ in the form

$$\tfrac{1}{2}(\mu_p + \mu_N)(\boldsymbol{\sigma}_p + \boldsymbol{\sigma}_N) + \tfrac{1}{2}(\mu_p - \mu_N)(\boldsymbol{\sigma}_p - \boldsymbol{\sigma}_N) \qquad (107)$$

and note that the first term gives no contribution to the matrix element (104). This follows from the fact that $(\boldsymbol{\sigma}_p + \boldsymbol{\sigma}_N)$, operating on the spin function χ_1, reproduces χ_1 multiplied by a constant factor, whereas we wish to produce χ_0.

Both the electric and magnetic cross sections decrease as $E^{-3/2}$ at high energies $E \gg W_1 = 2.19$ Mev, but the magnetic cross section is smaller by a factor of about

$$\frac{\sigma_m}{\sigma_{\text{el.}}} \simeq \frac{1}{4} \frac{W_1}{Mc^2} (\mu_p - \mu_N)^2 \tag{108}$$

$$\simeq \frac{1}{4} \frac{2.19}{931} (2.79 + 1.91)^2 = 0.013 = 1.3 \text{ per cent}$$

The smallness of this factor results from the smallness of the magnetic dipole moment $e\hbar/2Mc$ compared with the electric

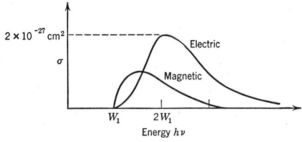

FIG. 11.   Photoelectric and photomagnetic cross sections of the deuteron as a function of energy.

dipole moment $ez/2$, because the deuteron is large in size compared to a proton Compton wave length.

At low energies ($E \ll W_1 = 2.19$ Mev) the electric cross section behaves as $E^{3/2}$, whereas the magnetic cross section behaves as $E^{1/2}/(E + W_0)$. Thus, for energies sufficiently near the threshold, the magnetic cross section will dominate by a factor

$$\frac{\sigma_m}{\sigma_{\text{el.}}} = \left[\frac{1}{4} \frac{W_1}{Mc^2} (\mu_p - \mu_N)^2 \right] \frac{W_1}{E} \frac{W_1}{W_0 + E}$$

$$= 0.013 \frac{W_1}{E} \frac{W_1}{W_0 + E} \tag{109}$$

For the 2.62-Mev γ-rays of ThC' the theoretical ratio of magnetic to electric cross sections is 0.27 (Schwinger and Rarita, Phys. Rev. **59**, 436). Approximate computation using equation 109 gives 0.29.

A rough plot of these cross sections as a function of energy is shown in Fig. 11. The maximum photoelectric cross section, at

$h\nu = 2W_1$, is about 2×10^{-27} cm^2, and the cross section at 100 Mev is somewhat under 10^{-28} cm^2.

EXPERIMENTS ON PHOTODISINTEGRATION

The first observations of the photodisintegration of the deuteron were made in a cloud chamber, using the 2.62-Mev γ-rays from ThC′ (Chadwick and Goldhaber, Nature **134**, 237, 1935). The determination of the cross section in this way is difficult: the sensitive time of a cloud chamber is hard to determine, and also a large error in the measured γ-ray intensity is possible. As more measurements were made the total cross section for photodisintegration grew from a value, 5×10^{-28} cm^2, in the initial experiments to 10×10^{-28} cm^2 (Halban, Compt. Rend. **206**, 1170, 1938). This is still not in satisfactory agreement with the theoretical value 15×10^{-28} cm^2 (Rarita and Schwinger, Phys. Rev. **59**, 436).

Chadwick, Feather, and Bretscher found in 1937 (Proc. Roy. Soc. (London) **A163**, 366) that the *angular distribution* of the 65 recoiling proton tracks in their cloud-chamber photographs was compatible with a sin$^2 \theta$ law (equation 100). This was slightly disconcerting because meanwhile it had been shown that the photomagnetic effect, which leads to a uniform distribution in angle, gives an appreciable contribution to the cross section at 2.62 Mev. Later measurements by Halban (1938) of the intensity of neutrons in the forward direction gave an upper limit for the photomagnetic cross section 0.9×10^{-28} cm at 2.62 Mev, as compared to a theoretical value of about 3×10^{-28}. However, in 1945 Graham and Halban (Rev. Modern Phys. **17**, 297) found slightly *more* neutrons in the forward direction than the theory just given predicts. Therefore, there is now sufficient agreement between experiment and the theory of Rarita and Schwinger. These authors have also pointed out further isotropic contributions arising from the tensor forces. The accuracy of present measurements would have to be improved by a factor of 100 to detect these small corrections.

CAPTURE OF NEUTRONS BY PROTONS

This is the process inverse to photodisintegration. The cross section for capture can be obtained from that for photodisintegration by statistical considerations such as those which will follow.

Consider a box containing protons, neutrons, deuterons, and γ-rays in equilibrium. Let state 1 consist of deuteron and γ-ray and state 2 of neutron and proton. Then at equilibrium

$$v_1 c_{1 \to 2} \times [\text{number of states 1}]$$

$$= v_2 \sigma_{2 \to 1} \times [\text{number of states 2}] \quad (110)$$

This equation will still hold if the brackets are replaced by the density of states per unit energy. This quantity is in general

$$\frac{4 \pi p^2}{(2 \pi \hbar)^3} \frac{dp}{dE} g \quad (111)$$

per unit volume of the box, where p is the momentum and g is the statistical weight of the states. Using the relativistic relations

$$\frac{E^2}{c^2} = p^2 + m^2 c^2, \quad \frac{dp}{dE} = \frac{E}{c^2 p} \quad \text{and} \quad \frac{Ev}{c^2} = p \quad (112)$$

equation 110 becomes

$$\frac{\sigma_{2 \to 1}}{\sigma_{1 \to 2}} = \frac{g_1}{g_2} \frac{p_1 v_1 E_1}{p_2 v_2 E_2} = \frac{g_1}{g_2} \frac{{p_1}^2}{{p_2}^2} \quad (113)$$

This is a general relation. To apply it to the definitions of states 1 and 2, set

$g_1 = g_{\text{deuteron}} g_{\gamma\text{-ray}}$, $p_1 = p_\gamma = \hbar \omega / c$, $\omega = 2\pi \times$ γ-ray frequency.

$g_2 = g_{\text{neutron}} g_{\text{proton}}$, $p_2 = p_{N,p} = Mv/2$, $M =$ proton or neutron mass.

$v =$ relative velocity of proton and neutron.

g_{deuteron} is 3 for the state $S = 1$, corresponding to the three possible directions of the spin. $g_{\gamma\text{-ray}}$ is 2, corresponding to the two possible directions of polarization of the photon. g_{neutron} and g_{proton} are each 2, corresponding to the two directions of spin. Using expression 105 for σ_m, we get

$$\sigma_{\text{capture}} = \pi \frac{e^2}{Mc^2} \frac{\hbar}{Mc} \sqrt{\frac{2W_1}{E_0}} \frac{(\sqrt{W_1} + \sqrt{W_0})^2 (W_1 + \tfrac{1}{2} E_0)}{(W_0 + \tfrac{1}{2} E_0) Mc^2} (\mu_p - \mu_N)^2 \quad (114)$$

where $E_0 / 2 = E = Mv^2 / 4 =$ energy of neutron and proton in the center-of-mass system. The σ_m has been used instead of the total photodisintegration cross section of the deuteron because $\sigma_{capture}$ will be appreciable only at low energies and here $\sigma_{el.}$ is small compared to σ_m. At very low energies $\sigma_{capture}$ is proportional to $E_0^{-\frac{1}{2}}$, i.e., to $1/v$. But $\sigma_{capture}v$ is proportional to the number of capture processes per unit time; therefore, the probability (per second) of capture of slow neutrons by protons is *independent of the neutron velocity* (also of the proton velocity, if any). At $E_0 \sim$ 0.025 ev, $\sigma_{capture} \sim 0.3$ barn according to theory; experiment agrees. This is a rather large capture cross section as capture cross sections go. This accounts for the fact that hydrogen is not used as a moderator in "piles," operating with normal uranium. Carbon and deuterium have capture cross sections about $1/100$ of that of hydrogen. One reason for the large value for hydrogen is the large size of $(\mu_p - \mu_N)$; another is the small size of W_0 (near-resonance at zero energy).

INFORMATION FROM LOW-ENERGY AND HIGH-ENERGY PHENOMENA

The account given so far of nuclear phenomena at low energies hangs together pretty well. Although at times during the development of the theory it seemed that every effect required a new ad hoc assumption, it now appears that the only assumptions needed are the binding energies of the triplet and the singlet states of the deuteron. The phenomena which can be explained quantitatively by these two constants are:

1. Binding energy of the ground state of the deuteron.

2. Cross section for neutron-proton scattering as a function of energy.

3. Angular distribution of neutron-proton scattering.

4. Scattering of neutrons by ortho- and para-hydrogen.

5. Photodisintegration cross section of the deuteron as a function of energy.

6. Angular distribution of resultant particles from photodisintegration of deuteron.

7. Capture cross section of neutrons and protons as a function of energy.

The success of the theory justifies the use of quantum mechanics for heavy particles and the use of a potential function $V(r)$, at least at low energies. Within limits the results at low energy were independent of the shape of $V(r)$ as long as it decreased rapidly with increasing r. If more information is wanted about the nuclear forces, the particles or photons must be given higher energies.

At higher energies the states of angular momentum $l \neq 0$ will enter into calculations of cross sections for scattering and photodisintegration. From the cross sections and the angular distributions of the resultant particles, one may hope to obtain:

1. $V(r)$ for $l = 0$ in more detail.
2. $V(r)$ for $l \neq 0$ as a function of l.

The energy necessary to give such information is sometimes higher than would appear from the simple arguments in Chapter IX.

For example, in neutron-proton scattering the energy 10 Mev might be presumed sufficient to determine the phase shift δ_1. This must be raised to 20 Mev for the following reason: the scattering cross section is proportional to the absolute value squared of

$$f(\theta) = e^{2i\delta_0} - 1 + 3(e^{2i\delta_1} - 1) \cos \theta \qquad (115)$$

If δ_1 is small, $e^{2i\delta_1} - 1 = 2i\delta_1$ and the cross section becomes $|(\cos 2\delta_0 - 1) + i(\sin 2\delta_0 + 6\delta_1 \cos \theta)|^2 = (\cos 2\delta_0 - 1)^2 + (\sin 2\delta_0 + 6\delta_1 \cos \theta)^2$. The term of first order in δ_1 is proportional to $\sin 2\delta_0$, and, unfortunately, at 10 Mev $\delta_0 \sim \pi/2 (\cot \delta_0 = \alpha/k \sim 0)$. Therefore, it is only for larger k, corresponding to perhaps 20 Mev, that the δ_1 terms in the cross section contribute appreciably. The situation is further aggravated by the fact that around 10 Mev the $\cos \theta$ terms in triplet and singlet scattering have opposite sign and cancel approximately.

There will be some difficulty in interpreting the results of scattering experiments at high energies because the different phases must be disentangled from each other, but this cannot be helped. The photodisintegration at high energies ought to give some clean-cut evidence on the transitions $^3S \rightarrow {}^3P$ because for dipole transitions the spin does not change and the orbital momentum changes by one. Above about 70 Mev, one might expect to get an appreciable number of quadrupole transitions to the ^3D-state because the wave length $\lambdabar$ of the γ-rays becomes comparable to the range of the forces. These could be distinguished from the dipole transitions by the angular distributions of resulting protons and neutrons.

XII. SCATTERING OF PROTONS BY PROTONS

No stable state of He^2 is observed, and this is supported theoretically by the fact that the potential energy function for the proton-proton interaction which is derived from proton-proton scattering experiments leads to no bound state. Thus proton-proton scattering is the only way to get direct evidence on proton-proton forces. Proton-proton scattering experiments are easier to perform and interpret than proton-neutron experiments, for the following reasons:

1. Protons are readily available.

2. Protons can be made monochromatic in energy. Neutrons made by the reaction $D + D \rightarrow He^3 + n$ can be expected to be monochromatic only up to about 6 Mev, where it begins to be possible to leave He^3 disintegrated into $H + D$. The best reaction to produce monochromatic neutrons is $D + H^3 \rightarrow He^4 + n$; this would be good to about 20 Mev, but at present tritium is not generally available.

3. Protons can be produced in well-collimated beams. Fast neutron beams are very hard to collimate.

4. Protons are easily detected by their ionization, which makes possible more accurate measurements of angular distribution than for neutrons.

5. Protons undergo Coulomb scattering simultaneously with nuclear scattering. This might seem to be a disadvantage, but actually it permits a determination of the interference between nuclear and Coulomb scattering and this makes for greater sensitivity (in case one of the scattering probabilities is small) and also allows a determination of the sign of the phase shifts resulting from the nuclear scattering. Further, the Coulomb scattering is well known theoretically and experimentally and can be used to calibrate the nuclear scattering measurements.

6. The proton-proton combination obeys Fermi statistics, whereas in the neutron-proton combination, states symmetric with respect to particle interchange as well as antisymmetric states

occur. This simplifies the analysis of proton-proton scattering, but of course neutron-proton scattering still must be measured in order to get complete information.

THEORY OF PROTON-PROTON SCATTERING

The theory of proton-proton scattering is more complicated than that of neutron-proton scattering because of the presence of the Coulomb potential in addition to the nuclear potential. The Coulomb potential requires a rather special wave-mechanical treatment of the scattering problem because of the slow variation of the potential with distance.

Scattering by Coulomb Field. Rutherford first investigated the scattering by a Coulomb field from the classical standpoint. His result is well known:

$$d\sigma = [e^4 Z_1^2 Z_2^2 / 4m^2 v^4 \sin^4 (\theta/2)] 2\pi \sin \theta \, d\theta \qquad (116)$$

where $Z_1 e$ and $Z_2 e$ are the charges of the particles, v is the velocity of the incident particle, m is the reduced mass, and θ is the scattering angle in the center-of-mass system. For two protons, $Z_1 = Z_2 = 1$, $m = M/2$, $\theta/2 = \theta_1$ (laboratory system). In the laboratory system equation 116 then becomes:

$$d\sigma = (e^4/E_0^2)(1/\sin^4 \theta_1 + 1/\cos^4 \theta_1) \cos \theta_1 \, 2\pi \sin \theta_1 \, d\theta_1 \quad (117)$$

The term containing $\cos^4 \theta_1$ is added because each proton at angle θ_1 in the laboratory system is accompanied by a recoil proton at angle $(\pi/2 - \theta_1)$ and these recoil protons are not counted in equation 116. A factor $4 \cos \theta_1$ arises from the transformation of the solid angle from the center-of-mass system to the laboratory system. $E_0 = \frac{1}{2} M v^2$ is the kinetic energy in the laboratory system.

As is well known, the Rutherford equation (116) agrees with the experimental results for the scattering of low-energy α-particles or protons by nuclei, the effect of the nuclear potential being negligible at these low energies. However, even at fairly low energies, the classical equation (117) does not give the correct scattering of protons *by protons.* One reason for this is the neglect of symmetry requirements by the classical theory. The wave-mechanical treatment of scattering in a Coulomb field by Mott showed that the correct result for identical scatterer and incident particle is:

$$d\sigma = \frac{e^4}{E_0{}^2} \left(\frac{1}{\sin^4 \theta_1} + \frac{1}{\cos^4 \theta_1} \right.$$

$$\left. - \frac{\cos [(e^2/\hbar v) \ln \tan^2 \theta_1]}{\sin^2 \theta_1 \cos^2 \theta_1} \right) \cos \theta_1 \, 2\pi \sin \theta_1 \, d\theta_1 \quad (118)$$

(see Mott and Massey, *Theory of Atomic Collisions*, p. 75). The extra term comes in because the identity of scattered particle and scatterer places symmetry requirements on the wave function. This term represents interference between the two parts of the wave function describing the two-proton system. The sign is negative because protons obey Fermi statistics. For unlike particles these terms drop out and the equation agrees exactly with the Rutherford equation (116).

For proton energies of 1 Mev and higher ($v > c/20$), $e^2/\hbar v < \frac{1}{7}$, so $\cos [(e^2/\hbar v) \ln \tan^2 \theta_1]$ is nearly unity except for θ_1 nearly zero or nearly $\pi/2$. Except in these regions, equation 118 is approximately

$$d\sigma = \frac{e^4}{E_0{}^2} \left(\frac{1}{\sin^4 \theta_1} + \frac{1}{\cos^4 \theta_1} \right.$$

$$\left. - \frac{1}{\sin^2 \theta_1 \cos^2 \theta_1} \right) \cos \theta_1 \, 2\pi \sin \theta_1 \, d\theta_1 \quad (119)$$

However, experiments of White, and of Tuve, Heydenburg, and Hafstad in 1936 indicated considerably more protons at 45° than given by equation 119 at proton energies of about 1 Mev. This indicates that the nuclear potential already has an appreciable effect.

Effect of Nuclear Potential. It is reasonable to assume that the nuclear potential between two protons has the same characteristics as that between neutron and proton. The Wigner argument about short-range forces (Chapter VII) involves both proton-proton and neutron-proton forces. The main difference between proton and neutron seems to be the electric charge, and the nuclear force apparently does not arise from charge. We assume therefore that the potential between two protons is confined within some short range a as before, although the value of a need not necessarily be the same.

Therefore, in proton-proton scattering *at low energies* it is expected that only the $l = 0$ scattering processes will be affected by the nuclear potential, just as in neutron-proton scattering.

We shall now merely outline the solution of the problem. (See Mott and Massey, *Theory of Atomic Collisions*, for a more complete development.)

In a purely Coulomb field, and in the center-of-mass system, an asymptotic solution of the Schrödinger equation for the scattering of two particles of equal mass M, one of which has an energy $\tfrac{1}{2}Mv^2$, is:

$$\psi(\mathbf{r}) = \exp\left[ikz + i\alpha \ln k(r - z)\right]$$
$$+ (g(\theta)/r) \exp\left(ikr - i\alpha \ln 2kr + i\pi + 2i\,\eta_0\right) \quad (120)$$

where

$$g(\theta) = [e^2/Mv^2 \sin^2 (\theta/2)] \exp\left[-i\alpha \ln \sin^2 (\theta/2)\right] \quad (120a)$$

and

$$\alpha = e^2/\hbar v, \quad k = Mv/2\hbar, \quad e^{i\eta_0} = \Gamma(1 + i\alpha)/\left|\Gamma(1 \mp i\alpha)\right| \quad (120b)$$

The first term in equation 120 is the incident wave: an almost plane wave with a small space-dependent phase shift caused by the long-range nature of the Coulomb potential. The second term is the spherical scattered wave. The square of the absolute value of $g(\theta)$ gives the cross section per unit solid angle, $d\sigma/d\Omega$, when there are no symmetry requirements on ψ. Note that $|g(\theta)|^2$ agrees exactly with equation 116, which is, therefore, correct for scattering of unlike particles with a pure Coulomb field.

Now if the effect of the nuclear force is considered without taking into account the identity of the particles, it is necessary to correct only the $l = 0$ component of the wave $\psi(\mathbf{r})$, equation 120. Let $\psi(\mathbf{r})$ be expanded in Legendre polynomials of $\cos\theta$:

$$\psi(\mathbf{r}) = (1/r) \sum_l v_l(r) P_l(\cos\theta) \quad (121a)$$

and let the true wave function $\chi(\mathbf{r})$, which includes the effect of the nuclear forces, be also expanded:

$$\chi(\mathbf{r}) = (1/r) \sum_l u_l(r) P_l(\cos\theta) \quad (121b)$$

No ϕ dependence is required because the incident wave is along the z axis (axis of the polar coordinate system). Such expansions are possible because both the Coulomb and the nuclear potentials are central. The lth term in the sums is the component of the wave with angular momentum l. $v_l(r)$ and $u_l(r)$ are solutions of the radial Schrödinger equation with pure Coulomb potential and with Coulomb-plus-nuclear potential, respectively. (See Fig. 12.) Thus $v_0(r)$ and $u_0(r)$ can be found; when they are calculated, it is found that asymptotically as $z \to \infty$, $u_0(kr) = v_0(kr + \delta_0)$, where δ_0 is a constant phase shift.

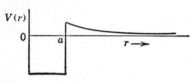

FIG. 12. Combined Coulomb potential and nuclear well. (Coulomb ignored inside well.)

Since we are correcting only the $l = 0$ term, we may write

$$\chi(\mathbf{r}) = \psi(\mathbf{r}) + (1/r)[u_0(r) - v_0(r)] \tag{122}$$

When $u_0(r)$ and $v_0(r)$ are normalized correctly, it is found that

$$\chi(\mathbf{r}) = \exp\,[ikz + i\alpha \ln k(r - z)]$$
$$+ (1/r) \exp\,[ikr - i\alpha \ln 2kr + i\pi + 2i\eta_0]f(\theta) \tag{123}$$

where

$$f(\theta) = \frac{e^2}{Mv^2} \frac{\exp\,[-i\alpha \ln \sin^2\,(\theta/2)]}{\sin^2\,(\theta/2)} + \frac{i}{2k}\,(e^{2i\delta_0} - 1) \tag{124}$$

The difference between this $f(\theta)$ and the $g(\theta)$ of equation 120b is the added term containing δ_0 which describes the nuclear scattering.

Symmetry of Wave Function. Equations 123 and 124 give the correct results for the scattering of unlike particles with a Coulomb potential. We must now correct these equations to account for the identity of the two protons. The spatial wave function must be either symmetrical, with total spin = 0, or antisymmetrical, with total spin = 1. Now $\chi(\mathbf{r})$ of equation 123 is neither symmetrical nor antisymmetrical. But

$$\chi_s = (1/\sqrt{2})[\chi(\mathbf{r}) + \chi(-\mathbf{r})] \tag{125a}$$

is obviously symmetrical and

$$\chi_a = (1/\sqrt{2})[\chi(\mathbf{r}) - \chi(-\mathbf{r})] \tag{125b}$$

is obviously antisymmetrical. Replacing $(\mathbf{r})$ by $(-\mathbf{r})$ is equivalent to replacing r by r, z by $-z$, and θ by $(\pi - \theta)$. If the expansion (121b) is considered and it is remembered that

$$P_l[\cos (\pi - \theta)] = (-1)^l P_l (\cos \theta) \tag{126}$$

it is seen that in 125a components with odd l drop out, whereas in 125b components with even l drop out. The $f(\theta)$'s for χ_s and χ_a are:

$$f_s(\theta) = \frac{e^2}{Mv^2} \left\{ \frac{\exp\left[-i\alpha \ln \sin^2 (\theta/2)\right]}{\sin^2 (\theta/2)} \right.$$
$$\left. + \frac{\exp\left[-i\alpha \ln \cos^2 (\theta/2)\right]}{\cos^2 (\theta/2)} \right\} + \frac{i}{k} (e^{2i\delta_0} - 1) \tag{127a}$$

$$f_a(\theta) = \frac{e^2}{Mv^2} \left\{ \frac{\exp\left[-i\alpha \ln \sin^2 (\theta/2)\right]}{\sin^2 (\theta/2)} \right.$$
$$\left. - \frac{\exp\left[-i\alpha \ln \cos^2 (\theta/2)\right]}{\cos^2 (\theta/2)} \right\} \tag{127b}$$

$f_s(\theta)$ comes from singlet $(S = 0)$ scattering, and $f_a(\theta)$ comes from triplet $(S = 1)$ scattering. The singlet and the triplet scattering add incoherently. Therefore, the total differential cross section is

$$d\sigma = [\tfrac{3}{4}|f_a(\theta)|^2 + \tfrac{1}{4}|f_s(\theta)|^2] \cdot 2\pi \sin \theta \, d\theta$$
$$= F(\theta) \cdot 2\pi \sin \theta \, d\theta \tag{128}$$

(definition of F).

To go to the laboratory system, replace θ by $2\theta_1$:

$$d\sigma = F(2\theta_1) \cdot 4 \cos \theta_1 \cdot 2\pi \sin \theta_1 \, d\theta_1 \tag{129}$$

From equations 127 to 129, and neglecting again the small exponents (a complete formula, including these terms, was given by Breit, Thaxton, and Eisenbud, Phys. Rev. **55**, 1018, 1939) in equation 127, the cross section per unit solid angle is

$$\frac{d\sigma}{d\Omega} = \frac{e^4}{E_0^2} \left[\frac{1}{\sin^4 \theta_1} + \frac{1}{\cos^4 \theta_1} - \frac{1}{\sin^2 \theta_1 \cos^2 \theta_1} \right.$$
$$\left. - \frac{2\hbar v}{e^2} \frac{\sin \delta_0 \cos \delta_0}{\sin^2 \theta_1 \cos^2 \theta_1} + \left(\frac{2\hbar v}{e^2}\right)^2 \sin^2 \delta_0 \right] \cos \theta_1 \tag{130}$$

Note that equation 130 reduces to the Mott formula (119) for a pure Coulomb field when δ_0 is zero, i.e., when there is no nuclear scattering.

The fourth term in the bracket in equation 130 is an interference term between Coulomb and nuclear scattering. This is a very useful term as it makes possible the experimental detection of quite small δ_0's because of the linear instead of quadratic dependence on δ_0.

The linearity in δ_0 of the interference term also permits determination of whether the nuclear potential is repulsive or attractive, as attractive potentials cause positive δ_0 and repulsive potentials cause negative δ_0. The experimental results indicate that the potential for $l = 0$ is attractive.

The last term in the bracket in equation 130 is exactly the scattering that would result if only the nuclear potential were present. For large energies this pure nuclear scattering becomes the most important because of the v^2 coefficient.

EXPERIMENTS ON PROTON-PROTON SCATTERING

Experiments thus far * have been published for energies up to 2.4 Mev. At this energy there is 43 times as much total scattering at $45°$ as Coulomb scattering. The most extensive experiments were carried out by Herb, Kerst, Parkinson, and Plain (Phys. Rev. **55**, 998) and analyzed by Breit, Thaxton, and Eisenbud (Phys. Rev. **55**, 1018).

From the observed angular distribution, the value of δ_0 is obtained, and an excellent check on the theory is provided by the requirement that the entire angular distribution must be fitted by a single parameter δ_0. This condition was found to be fulfilled within a fraction of a per cent, demonstrating again the applicability of quantum mechanics to such problems.

Having obtained δ_0 as a function of energy, Breit and his collaborators then derived a potential to fit these data. The potential is, of course, not uniquely determined. However, the experimental data were of sufficient accuracy to specify the well depth to ± 1 per cent for any assumed range. On the other hand, the range can only be fixed to about ± 15 per cent, similarly to the

---

* R. R. Wilson *et al.* have investigated the scattering at 10 and 14.5 Mev (Phys. Rev. **71**, 384 and 560, 1947). See Chapter XIV.—*Note added in proof.*

neutron-proton scattering. Assuming a rectangular well, the best fit is obtained for a range $a = 2.8 \times 10^{-13}$; for this range the depth is $V_0 = 10.5 \pm 0.1$ Mev. The exact shape of the well cannot be deduced at all from the experimental data.

More information about range and shape can be expected at higher energies, as shown in Fig. 12 of Breit's paper. At higher energies, also higher l components will be affected by the nuclear potential. For these cases the preceding theory must be extended to include the phase shifts δ_1, δ_2, etc., which are defined similarly to δ_0. The sign of δ_1 will indicate whether the potential for $l = 1$ is attractive or repulsive. δ_1 is still quite small (~ 0.1) at 10 Mev.

Lower proton energies are also useful for the determination of the range. In particular, at energies around 400 kev, the scattering at $45°$ is much *less* than the Coulomb scattering and very sensitive to the range. Ragan, Kanne, and Tashek (Phys. Rev. **60**, 621, 1941) have carried out such experiments and found $a = 2.8 \times 10^{-13}$ cm ± 15 per cent.

From the well depth 10.5 Mev found above for the ^1S potential (as stated before, symmetry requirements exclude a ^3S-state) it can be shown that there is no bound state for two protons. Thus He^2 is not stable against disintegration into two protons.

It is now worth while to compare the proton-proton well depth with the neutron-proton well depth for the ^1S-state. For $a = 2.8 \times 10^{-13}$ cm,

$$\text{Neutron-proton} \begin{cases} ^1S & V_0 = 11.9 \text{ Mev} \\ ^3S & V_1 = 21.3 \text{ Mev} \end{cases}$$

$$\text{Proton-proton} \quad ^1S \quad V_2 = 10.5 \text{ Mev}$$

For the ^1S-state, for which a comparison is possible, the potential V_2 for proton-proton is a little smaller than V_0 for neutron-proton. Breit has shown that this difference may almost be removed if the Coulomb potential is allowed to continue inside of the well (as it must be expected to do) instead of ignoring it, as in Fig. 12. We then conclude that neutron-proton forces and proton-proton forces are equal (except for Coulomb force), at least in the singlet S-state.

There is also evidence that neutron-neutron forces and proton-proton forces are equal (barring the Coulomb force) because of the success of this assumption in predicting the size of nuclei from the observed difference in binding energies of mirror nuclei. (See Chapter II, paragraph 3.)   Thus the forces

$$(\text{Neutron} - \text{Neutron}) = (\text{Proton} - \text{Neutron})$$

$$= (\text{Proton} - \text{Proton})$$

in the ^1S-state.

XIII. NON-CENTRAL FORCES

Central forces, i.e., forces which depend only on the distance between particles, have been adequate, so far, to explain binding energy and scattering experiments involving neutrons and protons. The existence of an electric quadrupole moment for the deuteron indicates a cigar-shaped distribution of charge which is not explainable by a central force. A force is needed which not only depends on the separation between neutron and proton, but also depends on the angle which their spins make with the line joining the two particles. This interaction potential must have the form $S_{12} V(r)$, where

$$S_{12} = 3(\sigma_1 \cdot \mathbf{r})(\sigma_2 \cdot \mathbf{r})/r^2 - \sigma_1 \cdot \sigma_2 \qquad (131)$$

The first term gives the dependence of the interaction on spin angles. The second term has been subtracted so that the average of S_{12} over all directions $\mathbf{r}$ is zero. Formula 131 has the same dependence on direction as the interaction of two dipoles σ_1 and σ_2.

The non-central or tensor interaction (131) has been justified on very general grounds by Wigner (Proc. Nat. Acad. Sci. **27**, 282, 1941). He has shown that if the interactions are assumed to be invariant with respect to displacement, rotation, and inversion of the observer's coordinate system, as well as independent of the particle velocities, the most general interaction can be written in the form

$$V_1(r) + V_2(r) \, \sigma_1 \cdot \sigma_2 + V_3(r) \, S_{12} \qquad (132)$$

where the potentials V may depend on the orbital momentum of the two particle system, as well as on the charge of the particles. (See also Rarita and Schwinger, Phys. Rev. **59**, 436, 1941.)

The reason for such a limited choice of interactions comes from the requirement of invariance against rotation and inversion (change of sign of all spatial coordinates). Thus the Cartesian components of σ_1 and σ_2 are not invariant against rotation, but $\sigma_1 \cdot \sigma_2$ is. On the other hand, $(\sigma \cdot \mathbf{r})$ is invariant against rotation, but not against inversion since $\mathbf{r} \to -\mathbf{r}$ and $\sigma \to \sigma$ on inversion. (σ behaves like an angular momentum $\mathbf{r} \times \mathbf{p} \rightarrow (-\mathbf{r}) \times (-\mathbf{p})$). Because of this, only even powers of $(\boldsymbol{\sigma} \cdot \mathbf{r})$ may occur such as $(\boldsymbol{\sigma}_1 \cdot \mathbf{r})(\boldsymbol{\sigma}_2 \cdot \mathbf{r})$. However, higher powers than the second may be shown from the commutation relationships of the spin operators to be reducible to the second power or less, provided the spin of each particle is $\frac{1}{2}$. Thus equation 132 constitutes the most general interaction.

STATES OF THE DEUTERON

Central forces of the form

$$V_1(r) + V_2(r)\boldsymbol{\sigma}_1 \cdot \boldsymbol{\sigma}_2 \tag{133}$$

are invariant with respect to rotations of space and spin coordinates *separately*. Since $\mathbf{L}$ and $\mathbf{S}$ correspond to infinitesimal rotation operators for space and spin coordinates (see Kemble, *Quantum Mechanics*, 1937, p. 306) these operators commute with the Hamiltonian formed by using the expression 133 as the potential. Since L_z and S_z commute with H, both m_L and m_s represent good quantum numbers, or constants of the motion. Although L_x and L_y commute with H, they do not commute with L_z and thus cannot be quantized simultaneously with it. On the other hand $\mathbf{L}^2$ commutes with both H and L_z and has the quantized eigenvalues $\hbar^2 L(L + 1)$. Similar statements apply to $\mathbf{S}^2$. Thus the quantum numbers of a state, with a Hamiltonian containing only central forces, are L, S, m_L, and m_s.

If non-central forces of the type S_{12} are present the Hamiltonian is invariant only under the *coupled* rotation of space and spin coordinates (rotation of the observer's point of view). Thus L and S are not in general expected to commute with the Hamiltonian, but $\mathbf{J} = \mathbf{L} + \mathbf{S}$ still must. Therefore J and m_J will be good quantum numbers.

Although S is not in general expected to be a good quantum number, it will be in this particular case involving *two particles*, *both of spin* $\frac{1}{2}$, for the Hamiltonian is symmetric in the spins of the two particles. From this, it follows, in a manner analogous to the discussion of parity given later, that the wave functions must be either *symmetric or antisymmetric in the spin coordinates* of the two particles. Thus the spin wave functions correspond to triplet or singlet states, and S is a good quantum number, even though m_s is not.

Parity. The Hamiltonian is also invariant with respect to inversion, i.e., replacement of $\mathbf{r} = \mathbf{r}_1 - \mathbf{r}_2$ by $-\mathbf{r}$. Thus the space wave-functions must be either even or odd with respect to inversion. This fact is commonly denoted as even or odd *parity* of the wave function. The statement that parity is a good quantum number will now be proven, in general, for a system containing any number of particles, assuming invariance of the Hamiltonian for inversion

$$H(-\mathbf{r}_k) = H(\mathbf{r}_k) \tag{134}$$

where the coordinates $\mathbf{r}_k$ of all the particles are inverted simultaneously. This assumption merely corresponds to the fact that all physical results should be independent of whether the observer uses a right- or left-handed coordinate system.

If we write Schrödinger's equation

$$H(\mathbf{r}_k)\psi(\mathbf{r}_k) = E\psi(\mathbf{r}_k) \tag{135}$$

and relabel all the coordinates $\mathbf{r}_k$ by $-\mathbf{r}_k$, we obtain:

$$H(-\mathbf{r}_k)\psi(-\mathbf{r}_k) = E\psi(-\mathbf{r}_k) \tag{136}$$

Using the symmetry of the Hamiltonian, we find

$$H(\mathbf{r}_k)\psi(-\mathbf{r}_k) = E\psi(-\mathbf{r}_k), \tag{137}$$

or $\psi(-\mathbf{r}_k)$ satisfies the same differential equation as $\psi(\mathbf{r}_k)$. Disregarding degeneracies, for a given energy, the two solutions must be proportional to each other

$$\psi(-\mathbf{r}_k) = K\psi(\mathbf{r}_k) \tag{138}$$

where K is a constant. Applying this operation twice,

$$\psi(\mathbf{r}_k) = K^2\psi(\mathbf{r}_k) \tag{139}$$

$$K = \pm 1 \tag{140}$$

Thus according to equations 138 and 140 parity is a good quantum number, i.e., all wave functions are either even or odd on inversion (i.e., they either remain unchanged or change sign). For the deuteron, therefore, there are four good quantum numbers: J, m_J, S, and parity.

Absence of Electric Dipole Moments. An interesting consequence of the fact that parity is a good quantum number is that nuclei cannot have electric dipole moments. The definition of the dipole moment is

$$\mathbf{D} = \int \sum_j e_j \mathbf{r}_j \left| \psi(\mathbf{r}_k) \right|^2 \, d\tau_k \tag{141}$$

If in this formula we introduce new variables $\mathbf{r}_k \rightarrow -\mathbf{r}_k$, the first factor changes sign whereas the second one, because of parity, remains identically the same. Thus $\mathbf{D} = -\mathbf{D}$, or $\mathbf{D} = 0$.

For a two-particle system *even parity* corresponds to a superposition of *even* L's and *odd parity* corresponds to a superposition of *odd* L's. Thus states of even and odd L do not mix. Now the only possible values of S are $S = 0$ and $S = 1$. But if $S = 0$, $L = J$ and thus L in this instance is a good quantum number. On the other hand, if $S = 1$, the laws of addition of angular momenta permit $L = J - 1, J, J + 1$. However, $L = J$ has opposite parity to that of $L = J - 1, J + 1$, so that $S = 1, L = J$ defines a state by itself, and the state of opposite parity will have $S = 1$ with a mixture of $L = J + 1$ and $L = J - 1$. Therefore, for a given J the possible states are in spectroscopic notation: ^1J_J, ^3J_J, and the mixture $^3(J - 1)_J + {}^3(J + 1)_J$. In particular, we have the following states of small J:

$$
\begin{array}{cccc}
J = 0 & {}^1S_0 & {}^3P_0 & \\
J = 1 & {}^1P_1 & {}^3P_1 & {}^3S_1 + {}^3D_1 \\
J = 2 & {}^1D_2 & {}^3D_2 & {}^3P_2 + {}^3F_2
\end{array}
$$

The ground state of the deuteron has a measured total angular momentum of $J = 1$, and consists primarily of the triplet state $^3S_1$. When non-central forces are taken into account, therefore, it becomes the $^3S_1 + {}^3D_1$ state.

DETERMINATION OF FORCE CONSTANTS

In order to obtain quantitative results, Rarita and Schwinger (Phys. Rev. **59**, 436, 1941) have made extensive calculations using the potential

$$
V = \begin{cases}
-V_0[(1 - g/2) + (g/2)\sigma_1 \cdot \sigma_2 + \gamma S_{12}] & r < a \\
0 & r > a
\end{cases} \tag{142}
$$

with the constants g and γ, in addition to V_0 and a, to be determined from experiment. This potential uses square wells of the same radius a, for each of the potentials V_1, V_2, and V_3 of equation 132, but of depths in the ratios

$$(1 - g/2) : g/2 : \gamma$$

Some restriction like that of equal radius a has to be made on the form of V_1, V_2, and V_3, in order to make calculations possible. The experimental data were and are at present sufficiently limited so that it is possible to determine only a small number of arbitrary parameters in V; here these are a, V_0, g, and γ. (The use of the particular definition in equation 142, especially of $V_0(1 - g/2)$ for the spin-independent term rather than simply V_0, is devoid of physical meaning.)   For the calculations, Rarita and Schwinger chose $a = 2.80 \times 10^{-13}$ cm, in accord with proton-proton scattering * (Chapter XII).   The remaining parameters are determined from

(1) the binding energy of the ground state of the deuteron,

(2) the scattering of slow neutrons by free protons, and

(3) the quadrupole moment of the deuteron, Q.

First, V_0 and γ are determined from (1) and (3); g does not enter the calculation since, for the $^3S_1$ and $^3D_1$ states, which are mixed to form the deuteron ground state, $\sigma_1 \cdot \sigma_2 = +1$; and the terms in g in the potential V cancel each other.   For a given V_0, the γ is chosen so that the ground state has the proper binding energy then the ground-state wave function yields the relative percentages of $^3S_1$ and $^3D_1$ state and a value of Q.   For example,

V_0 (Mev)	γV_0 (Mev)	$Q(10^{-27}$ cm^2)
21	0	0
14	10	2.67
0	20	3.71
−15	29	4.26

(For further values, see Rarita and Schwinger, Phys. Rev. **59**, 436 Table II, 1941.)

The observed value of Q, 2.73×10^{-27} cm^2, gives $V_0 = 13.8$ Mev and $\gamma = 0.775$, and corresponds to 3.9 per cent of D state in probability or ~20 per cent in amplitude.   (This was the value used in Chapter VII in the discussion of the magnetic moments.) The ground state can be made stable even when the central force

* In view of the results of ortho- and para-hydrogen scattering (Chapter X) the assumption of equal range for all three potentials is somewhat doubtful.

is repulsive ($V_0 < 0$), by the use of a sufficient amount of non-central force. The value of Q is not particularly sensitive to the value of γ and therefore does not permit a very accurate determination of γ and V_0. The percentage of D state is nearly proportional to Q, and is therefore relatively well determined, once the assumption of rectangular wells of equal width is accepted.

Next, g is determined from the depth, 11.9 Mev, of the potential well for the singlet state. This depth comes from the observed scattering of slow neutrons in hydrogen (see Chapter IX). For the singlet state, $\sigma_1 \cdot \sigma_2 = -3$ and $S_{12} = 0$. Thus,

$$V = 11.9 \text{ Mev} = V_0(1 - 2g)$$

Using $V_0 = 13.8$ Mev, we get $g = 0.07$; this g is quite close to zero. g can be made exactly zero, if a be changed to 2.70×10^{-13} cm (which is certainly compatible with other evidence) whereas V_0 is determined to hold Q at 2.73×10^{-27} cm^2. [If we put $g = 0$ but retain $a = 2.80 \times 10^{-13}$ cm, then $V_0 = 11.9$ and $Q = 2.95 \times 10^{-27}$ cm^2. This value of Q is somewhat outside the experimental error of ± 0.05. It is an attractive idea to make $g = 0$ because this reduces the number of independent forces that have to be assumed.

Having now determined the values of the constants,

$$V_0 = 13.8 \text{ Mev}, \quad \gamma = 0.775, \quad g = 0.0715 \qquad (143)$$

the theory can be checked against the experiments of the list given at the end of Chapter XI. It will be remembered that these were in adequate agreement with the theory with central forces alone: therefore, the tensor forces must be proved to have no appreciable influence on the results. We are following in this proof the paper of Rarita and Schwinger; a more general proof, free from numerical calculations, has been given by Kepner and Peierls (Proc. Roy. Soc. **181**, 43, 1943).

NEUTRON-PROTON SCATTERING

At low energies, the scattering is almost the same as without tensor forces. The triplet scattering is attributable mainly to the $^3S_1$ part of the triplet state because the $^3D_1$ wave is small at small distances, for low energy. The quantitative results are:

$E = 0$, $\sigma_{\text{triplet}} = 4.21$ barns as compared with 4.30 with central forces.

$E = 2.8$ Mev, $\sigma_{\text{total}} = 2.53$ barns as compared with 2.56 with central forces. The old experimental value (quoted by Rarita and Schwinger) was 2.40 barns; newer experiments agree perfectly with theory. The tensor forces reduce the cross section slightly, for the presence of the ^3D state component decreases the percentage of ^3S state in the wave function without itself contributing appreciably to the scattering. The angular dependence of the total cross section is $(1 + 0.00559 \cos^2 \theta)$, which is isotropic as far as any experiments are concerned.

CAPTURE OF NEUTRONS BY PROTONS

For magnetic dipole capture, which is the only process of importance at low energies, the results are about the same as with central forces but agree slightly better with experiment.

For $E = 0.025$ ev (thermal neutrons), $\sigma = 0.302$ barn, as compared with 0.312 with central forces and 0.30 observed.

PHOTODISINTEGRATION OF THE DEUTERON

The photoelectric cross section at 2.62 Mev is 11.99×10^{-28} cm^2 as compared with 12.31 with central forces and about 8 according to the very inaccurate experiments. The angular dependence is $\sin^2 \theta + 0.0007$. The isotropic term results from transitions $^3D_1 \rightarrow {}^3P$ and is so small that it will probably never be observed.

The photomagnetic cross section at 2.62 Mev is 3.28×10^{-28} cm^2, with an angular distribution $(1 - 0.0035 \cos^2 \theta)$. The non-isotropic term results from ^3D to ^1D transitions and is well beyond experimental detection.

The total cross section at 2.62 Mev is 15.27×10^{-28} cm^2 with an angular dependence of $(\sin^2 \theta + 0.182)$. Graham and Halban give 10×10^{-28} cm^2 with an angular dependence $\sin^2 \theta + 0.26$ ± 0.08.

Thus for low energies, the use of non-central forces gives no appreciable change from the central force theory. To give a theory for higher energies at which states of $l \neq 0$ contribute essentially, the exchange properties of nuclear forces must be considered.

XIV. SATURATION OF NUCLEAR FORCES

The binding energy and volume of nuclei are proportional to A, the mass number. This is not in accord with a law of force which gives equal interactions between all pairs of particles in the nucleus, for there are then $A(A - 1)/2$ distinct interacting pairs and a binding energy at least proportional to $A(A - 1)/2$ might be expected, if not to a higher power of A due to increased packing with more interaction. Instead, the nuclear binding energies seem similar to the internal energies of bulk matter, in which 2 pounds has twice as much energy and volume as 1 pound.

To account for this phenomenon of "saturation of nuclear forces," in which one particle apparently interacts with only a limited number of others, various hypotheses have been made, and various other assumptions about the nature of the forces can be shown to be impossible.

Among the impossible assumptions is that which has been used in this book so far, namely, an ordinary potential independent of the angular momentum, because it is easily shown that such a potential does not give saturation. This is so even if the Coulomb repulsion of the protons is taken into account. The proof can be carried out with various degrees of exactness, using the variational method. This method is based on the Schrödinger variational theorem which states that the quantity

$$\Omega = \int \psi H \psi \, d\tau / \int \psi^2 \, d\tau \qquad (144)$$

is a minimum when ψ is the correct eigenfunction of the lowest eigenvalue E_0 of H, and the minimum value of Ω is E_0. Thus, if the assumed Hamiltonian operator representing the interaction of the particles in a given nucleus is sandwiched between any *arbitrary* ψ in the expression for Ω, the value of Ω must be greater (i.e., less negative) than the correct energy of that nucleus. The simplest ψ's are plane waves inside a box representing the nucleus. If the size of the box is adjusted to give as low an Ω as possible, this size comes out about equal to the range of nuclear forces, which is clearly much too small. Further, it gives a potential energy proportional to A^2, and a kinetic energy proportional to $A^{5/3}$. The size of the coefficients of these powers is such that the potential energy dominates for $A > 50$; for $A = 238$ the binding energy is greater than 238 mass units. This is convincing evidence that the ordinary potential will not work, and this is true independently of the shape of the potential (square well, exponential, Gaussian, etc.).

What is needed is a potential which prevents the particles from getting too close together. A potential repulsive at short distances, originally used by Morse for molecules, has been explored by Schiff and Fisk; the only objection is that the high repulsive potential may give relativistic difficulties if it gets above $2Mc^2 \sim 1800$ Mev, for a proton in such a state would have negative kinetic energy. However, the idea of a repulsive potential has not been followed up sufficiently.

EXCHANGE FORCES

In the first paper on nuclear forces, Heisenberg proposed, in order to explain the saturation of nuclear forces, that these forces are "exchange" forces, similar to the force that binds ordinary chemical molecules. Without inquiring into the origin of these exchange forces, let us write down the various types of exchange forces that can exist between two particles, and then examine the effects of these forces on the properties of the deuteron, and on the saturation of the binding energy.

For an ordinary (non-exchange) central force the Schrödinger equation for two particles is (in the center-of-mass system):

$$[(\hbar^2/M)\nabla^2 + E]\psi(\mathbf{r}_1, \mathbf{r}_2, \sigma_1, \sigma_2) = V(r)\psi(\mathbf{r}_1, \mathbf{r}_2, \sigma_1, \sigma_2) \quad (145)$$
$$Wigner$$

In nuclear physics, such forces are called Wigner forces. The interaction does not cause any exchange between coordinates of the two particles. Another type of interaction is one that interchanges the space coordinates of the two particles in addition to multiplication of ψ by some $V(r)$; for such an interaction, the Schrödinger equation is:

$$[(\hbar^2/M)\nabla^2 + E]\psi(\mathbf{r}_1, \mathbf{r}_2, \sigma_1, \sigma_2) = V(r)\psi(\mathbf{r}_2, \mathbf{r}_1, \sigma_1, \sigma_2) \quad (146)$$
$$Majorana$$

Such a force is called a Majorana force. Two other possibilities are: (1) the Bartlett force, with interchange of spin coordinates, and (2) the Heisenberg force, with interchange of both space and spin coordinates. The Schrödinger equations are respectively:

$$[(\hbar^2/M)\nabla^2 + E]\psi(\mathbf{r}_1, \mathbf{r}_2, \sigma_1, \sigma_2) = V(r)\psi(\mathbf{r}_1, \mathbf{r}_2, \sigma_2, \sigma_1) \quad (147)$$
Bartlett

$$[(\hbar^2/M)\nabla^2 + E]\psi(\mathbf{r}_1, \mathbf{r}_2, \sigma_1, \sigma_2) = V(r)\psi(\mathbf{r}_2, \mathbf{r}_1, \sigma_2, \sigma_1) \quad (148)$$
Heisenberg

Effects of Exchange Forces.   Exchange forces, with a $V(r)$, are central forces and do not cause mixing of l's. However, if a tensor force is used instead of $V(r)$ as the multiplying potential, l's are mixed and the quadrupole moment of the deuteron may be explained as before. It should be pointed out that the tensor force does not by itself lead to saturation; this was proved by Volkoff (Phys. Rev. **62**, 134).

Majorana Force.   The Majorana interaction replaces $(\mathbf{r})$ by $(-\mathbf{r})$ in ψ. Using the well-known behavior of the wave function on such an inversion, the Schrödinger equation (146) may be rewritten

$$[(\hbar^2/M)\nabla^2 + E]\psi(\mathbf{r}) = (-1)^l V(r)\psi(\mathbf{r}) \quad (149)$$

This is equivalent to having an ordinary potential that changes sign according to whether l is even or odd, and is independent of spin. Since the experimental data discussed so far give information on the potential only for $l = 0$, we have as yet no direct evidence as to whether the potential is "ordinary" or of the Majorana type. Since the potential is attractive for $l = 0$, it would be equally repulsive for $l = 1$ if the interaction were totally of the Majorana type.

Bartlett Force.   Considering still a system of two particles, the spin function is symmetric if the total spin S is 1, and antisymmetric if the total spin is 0. Thus, the Schrödinger equation (147) for the Bartlett force may be rewritten:

$$[(\hbar^2/M)\nabla^2 + E]\psi(\mathbf{r}) = (-1)^{S+1} V(r)\psi(\mathbf{r}) \quad (150)$$

This is equivalent to an ordinary potential which changes sign between $S = 0$ and $S = 1$. Since we know from neutron-proton scattering data that both the ^3S and ^1S potentials are attractive, the nuclear force cannot be totally of the Bartlett type.

Heisenberg Force. Combining the arguments of the two last paragraphs, the Schrödinger equation (148) may be rewritten for the Heisenberg force:

$$[(\hbar^2/M)\nabla^2 + E]\psi(\mathbf{r}) = (-1)^{l+S+1}V(r)\psi(\mathbf{r}) \qquad (151)$$

This is equivalent to an ordinary potential which changes sign according to whether $l + S$ is even or odd. For example, the effective potential is:

for	^3S	^1S	^3P	^1P	
potential	$+ V(r)$	$- V(r)$	$- V(r)$	$+ V(r)$	(152)

The reversal of sign between ^3S- and ^1S-states indicates, as for the Bartlett force, that the nuclear force cannot be wholly of the Heisenberg type. However, the difference between the ^3S and ^1S neutron-proton well depths (about 21 and 12 Mev, respectively, for $a = 2.8 \times 10^{-13}$ cm) can be explained by assuming that the interaction is about 25 per cent Heisenberg or Bartlett and 75 per cent Wigner or Majorana.

Exchange Forces and Saturation. The Bartlett spin-exchange force does not lead to saturation of the binding energy per particle. If the nuclear force were of the Bartlett type, heavy nuclei should exist with all spins aligned where the number of interacting pairs is $A(A - 1)/2$, which leads to binding energy proportional to at least the square of A.

However, the space exchange in the Majorana and the Heisenberg forces does lead to saturation because of the alternation in sign of the potential between odd and even l. For example, assume the nuclear force is the Majorana type (we already know it cannot be more than about 25 per cent Heisenberg). Then saturation should not be apparent in nuclei up to He[4], for in He[4] the spatial wave function can still be symmetrical in all four particles, without violating the Pauli principle. We need only give antiparallel spins (antisymmetric spin wave functions) to the two neutrons, and likewise to the two protons. Thus the Majorana force does not alter the Wigner argument about the short range of the forces based on the binding energies of He[4] and lighter nuclei.

In the next heavier nucleus—He[5] or Li[5]—the Pauli principle can no longer be satisfied by spin wave functions alone; therefore, the spatial wave function must have at least one node. In other words, only four particles can be in an s-state, whereas the last has to be put in a p-state, and will therefore be repelled by the other particles. He^5 and Li^5 should thus be unstable, in agreement with experiment. This is a first sign of saturation.

To investigate saturation in heavy nuclei, one may use the same variational method used at the beginning of the present chapter to prove that ordinary forces do *not* give saturation. It is satisfactory that this calculation, in the case of the Majorana force, does *not* lead to non-saturation. On the other hand, since the variational method gives only a maximum to the true energy, it cannot be used to prove that the Majorana force *does* give saturation. But Wigner has given a conclusive argument that saturation is achieved with the space-exchange Majorana force (Proc. Nat. Acad. Sci. **22**, 662, 1936). The space-exchange part of the Heisenberg force would also cause saturation.

SPIN AND ISOTOPIC SPIN

It is often convenient to write exchange forces in a slightly different way. Since for two particles

$$\sigma_1 \cdot \sigma_2 = +1 \text{ for } S = 1$$

$$= -3 \text{ for } S = 0, \tag{153}$$

the Bartlett force between two particles can obviously be written as

$$\tfrac{1}{2}V(r)(1 + \sigma_1 \cdot \sigma_2) = \begin{cases} +V(r), S = 1 \\ -V(r), S = 0 \end{cases} \tag{154}$$

The spin-exchange part of the Heisenberg force could be written in the same way.

In order to be able to use a similar notation for the space-exchange part of forces, we introduce the concept of the charge of a particle as a coordinate, i.e., neutron and proton are regarded as different eigenstates of the same particle, called a *nucleon*. We choose the symbol τ for this charge coordinate and we define

$$\left. \begin{array}{l} M_\tau \equiv \tfrac{1}{2} \text{ for the proton} \\ M_\tau \equiv -\tfrac{1}{2} \text{ for the neutron} \\ T \equiv \tfrac{1}{2} \text{ for both} \end{array} \right\} \tag{155}$$

using $\pm\frac{1}{2}$ in analogy with the spin coordinate. We also define the charge functions

$$\text{Charge function} = \gamma \text{ for the proton}$$
$$= \delta \text{ for the neutron} \tag{156}$$

in analogy with the spin functions α and β.

The nucleons must obey Fermi statistics in order to be consistent with the ordinary theory (this will become apparent shortly, if it is not immediately obvious). Thus the total wave function (including the charge function) for two or more particles

$$\psi = \psi_{\text{space}}(\mathbf{r}) \, \psi_{\text{spin}}(\sigma) \, \psi_{\text{charge}}(\tau) \tag{157}$$

must be antisymmetric with respect to interchange of *all* coordinates of two nucleons. We therefore look for symmetric and antisymmetric charge functions for two particles. There are four of these, as given in Table 4.

TABLE 4

Two-Particle Charge Functions

State	Function	Representing	Symmetry	Net Charge
I	$\gamma(1)\gamma(2)$	He^2	symmetric	$2e$
II	$\delta(1)\delta(2)$	n^2	symmetric	0
III	$(1/\sqrt{2})[\gamma(1)\delta(2) + \gamma(2)\delta(1)]$	H^2	symmetric	e
IV	$(1/\sqrt{2})[\gamma(1)\delta(2) - \gamma(2)\delta(1)]$	H^2	antisymmetric	e

Again, in analogy to spin, two quantum numbers are defined to describe these functions: T to describe symmetry, and M_τ to describe the net charge. These quantities have the values given in Table 5.

TABLE 5

Quantum Numbers for Charge States

State	T	M_τ
I	1	1
II	1	-1
III	1	0
IV	0	0

T is 1 for symmetric functions, 0 for the antisymmetric function, in analogy to spin. M_τ is the sum of the M_τ's for the two nucleons.

In the literature τ is called the "isotopic spin," T is called "the total isotopic spin," and M_τ may be called the "component of τ in the direction of positive charge." T is analogous to total spin S, and M_τ to S_z. For a given T, M_τ can have the values T, $T - 1$, $\cdots$, $-T$.

From Table 4 it is seen that a system containing two neutrons or two protons has a symmetric charge function. Since we are assuming nucleons to obey Fermi statistics, the remainder of the wave function (157) must be antisymmetric. This implies (correctly) Fermi statistics for neutrons and protons, disregarding charge as a coordinate. But in a system containing a neutron and a proton the charge function can be either symmetric or antisymmetric, and so also can the remainder of the wave function. Therefore, the treatment of proton and neutron as two eigenstates of the same particle does not in this case introduce any restrictions, consistent with the ordinary theory of statistics.

It is also convenient to introduce an operator τ in analogy to the σ operator, defined by its effect on the "charge coordinate" M_τ. The eigenvalue of its absolute square is, again in analogy with spin:

$$|\tau|^2 = 4T(T + 1) \tag{158}$$

Then, just as for spin, in a system of two nucleons

$$\begin{aligned} \tau_1 \cdot \tau_2 &= +1 \text{ for } T = 1 \\ &\quad -3 \text{ for } T = 0 \end{aligned} \tag{159}$$

Now the Heisenberg interaction can be written (letting $V(r)$ absorb the factor -1) as

$$\tfrac{1}{2} V(r)(1 + \tau_1 \cdot \tau_2) \tag{160}$$

To prove this, we note that equation 160 changes sign according to whether the charge part of the wave function (equation 157) is symmetric or antisymmetric, i.e., according to whether the product of space and spin functions is antisymmetric or symmetric, which is just what is required according to equations 151 and 152.

The types of interaction between the two particles discussed so far may now be summarized by listing the various types of operators, which when multiplied by some $V(r)$ give the interactions listed in Table 6.

Eisenbud and Wigner (Proc. Nat. Acad. Sci. **27**, 281) have shown that these interactions and their linear combinations are the only

TABLE 6

TYPES OF INTERACTIONS

Ordinary	1
Spin exchange	$\sigma_1 \cdot \sigma_2$
Space-spin exchange	$\tau_1 \cdot \tau_2$
Space exchange	$(\sigma_1 \cdot \sigma_2)(\tau_1 \cdot \tau_2)$
Tensor	$(\sigma_1 \cdot r)(\sigma_2 \cdot r)$
Tensor exchange	$(\sigma_1 \cdot r)(\sigma_2 \cdot r)(\tau_1 \cdot \tau_2)$

ones possible under certain reasonable invariance requirements, namely, excluding interactions depending on total charge or on the momentum. (The interaction $(\sigma_1 + \sigma_2) \cdot L$ depends on the momentum.)

QUANTITATIVE THEORY OF EXCHANGE FORCES

In the last chapter, it was shown that the ground state of the deuteron, the neutron-proton scattering, and the quadrupole moment of the deuteron could be obtained quantitatively by assuming a neutron-proton interaction of the form

$$V_{(even)} = -(1 - \tfrac{1}{2}g + \tfrac{1}{2}g\, \sigma_1 \cdot \sigma_2 + \gamma S_{12})J(r) \qquad (161)$$

with

$$J(r) = V_0 \qquad r < a$$

$$J(r) = 0 \qquad r > a$$

$$g = 0.0715 \qquad V_0 = 13.89 \text{ Mev}$$

$$\gamma = 0.775 \qquad a = 2.80 \times 10^{-13} \text{ cm}$$

—Rarita and Schwinger.

The neutron-proton interaction (161) applies only to states of $L = 0$. The potential for other L is as yet arbitrary. If we assume in particular a force of the type discussed in this chapter, i.e., depending only on the product of the isotopic spins $\tau_1 \cdot \tau_2$, the potential will depend only on the parity of the state. The potential for states of odd parity can only be determined from that for states of even parity by making some assumption regarding the exchange character (or dependence on $\tau_1 \cdot \tau_2$) of the forces. Rarita and Schwinger chose to investigate three potentials which were suggested by three types of meson theory (see Chapter XV):

    I. Symmetric meson theory.

    II. Exchange forces, or charged meson theory.

    III. Ordinary forces, or neutral meson theory.

These potentials are:

$$
\begin{array}{lll}
\text{I.} & V = -\tfrac{1}{3}\tau_1 \cdot \tau_2 \, \sigma_1 \cdot \sigma_2 \, V_{\text{even}} & \\
\text{II.} & V = \quad\quad (-1)^l \quad\quad V_{\text{even}} & \\
\text{III.} & V = \quad\quad\quad\quad\quad\quad V_{\text{even}} &
\end{array} \right\} \tag{162}
$$

where V_{even} is given in equation 161.

For ordinary forces III, the potential in odd states is the same as for even. Exchange forces II, on the other hand, have opposite sign in odd states. To determine the behavior of the force sug-

TABLE 7

PROPERTIES OF A NEUTRON-PROTON SYSTEM

State	Parity	Spin S	Isotopic Spin T	$\sigma_1 \cdot \sigma_2$	$\tau_1 \cdot \tau_2$
^1S	even	0	1	-3	1
^3S	even	1	0	$+1$	-3
^1P	odd	0	0	-3	-3
^3P	odd	1	1	$+1$	$+1$

gested by the symmetric theory I, Table 7 of values of $\sigma_1 \cdot \sigma_2$ and $\tau_1 \cdot \tau_2$ has been constructed for even and odd states of both the singlet and the triplet types.

From equation 162 and Table 7, the symmetric theory (I) gives:

$$
\begin{aligned}
{}^3V_{\text{odd}} &= -\tfrac{1}{3} \, {}^3V_{\text{even}} \\
{}^1V_{\text{odd}} &= -3 \, {}^1V_{\text{even}}
\end{aligned} \tag{163}
$$

The three types of forces may now be compared with experiments by computing neutron-proton scattering at high energy. The energy chosen by Rarita and Schwinger was 15.3 Mev, for which P-wave scattering begins to be important. The P-wave scattering is to be computed with the aid of equations 162 and 163, which give the potentials acting in the P-state. It should be noted that in contrast to the usual theory in which a single phase shift δ_1 is computed for scattering in the P-state, three phase shifts η_0, η_1, and η_2 must be computed for scattering by the $^3P_0$-, $^3P_1$-, and $^3P_2$-states, respectively. The reason for this is that the effective potential well for each of these three states differs because of the presence of the non-central tensor force S_{12}. In fact, the operator S_{12} has definite values (-4 and 2) for the states $^3P_0$ and $^3P_1$

TABLE 8

WELL DEPTHS IN THE NEUTRAL THEORY

State	Effective Well Depth with "Ordinary Forces"
$^3P_0$	29.2 Mev (repulsive)
$^3P_1$	-35.4 Mev (attractive)
$^3P_2$	$-\ 9.6$ Mev (attractive)

which occur unmixed and must therefore be eigenfunctions of S_{12}. The $^3P_2$-state has a fairly definite value of S_{12} ($-\frac{2}{5}$), since at 15.3 Mev it is only slightly coupled to the $^3F_2$-state. (See Chapter XIII for a discussion of how S_{12} couples states of different L but the same J.)

Rarita and Schwinger (Phys. Rev. **59**, 556, 1941), using equation 161 and the values of S_{12} just quoted, give the effective well depths for the ^3P-states in the neutral theory III as shown in Table 8.

TABLE 9

PHASE SHIFTS IN $^3P_0$, $^3P_1$, AND $^3P_2$ STATES

Theory	η_0	η_1	η_2
I	0.074	-0.054	-0.017
II	0.531	-0.114	-0.046
III	-0.102	0.995	0.073

The potentials of the charged theory II have opposite sign to the tabulated values; those of the symmetric theory I have opposite sign and are one-third as large. (See equations 162, 163.) The phase shifts for each of the three theories, using these well depths, are given in Table 9.

Note that the phase shifts in Table 9 for theory I are small because potentials are used which are only one-third as large as for theories II and III. (See equation 163.) Note also that the signs of the phase shifts are opposite in theories II and III because this is also true of their potentials. (See equation 162.) Note further that really large phase shifts occur only for strong attractive potentials, i.e., η_0 in theory II and η_1 in theory III.

If the scattering contributions from the ^3P-states are added up with the proper statistical weight $(2J + 1)$ the total scattering for ^3P-states at 15.3 Mev is found to be:

$$
\left.
\begin{array}{ll}
\text{I.} & \sigma(\theta) = \lambda^2 \ (0.0038 + 0.0045 \cos^2 \theta) \\[4pt]
\text{II.} & \sigma(\theta) = \lambda^2 \ (0.103 - 0.002 \cos^2 \theta) \\[4pt]
\text{III.} & \sigma(\theta) = \lambda^2 \ (0.487 + 0.687 \cos^2 \theta)
\end{array}
\right\} \quad (164)
$$

with $4\pi\lambda^2 = 0.682 \times 10^{-24}$ cm^2.

The scattering is also computed for the $(^3S_1 + {}^3D_1)$ state. This is added to equation 164, taking proper account of interference terms with the result that the total triplet scattering in barns becomes:

$$
\left.
\begin{array}{ll}
\text{I.} & \sigma(\theta) = 0.680 \ (0.983 + 0.002 \cos \theta + 0.051 \cos^2 \theta) \\[4pt]
\text{II.} & \sigma(\theta) = 0.746 \ (0.986 + 0.193 \cos \theta + 0.041 \cos^2 \theta) \\[4pt]
\text{III.} & \sigma(\theta) = 1.165 \ (0.857 + 0.849 \cos \theta + 0.429 \cos^2 \theta)
\end{array}
\right\} \quad (165)
$$

The quantities in equation 165 are so normalized that the numbers outside the parentheses represent the total cross sections.

A corresponding calculation for the ^1P and ^1S scattering gives:

$$
\left.
\begin{array}{ll}
\text{I.} & \sigma(\theta) = 0.444 \ (0.939 - 0.438 \cos \theta + 0.182 \cos^2 \theta) \\[4pt]
\text{II.} & \sigma(\theta) = 0.424 \ (0.985 - 0.240 \cos \theta + 0.044 \cos^2 \theta) \\[4pt]
\text{III.} & \sigma(\theta) = 0.437 \ (0.955 + 0.498 \cos \theta + 0.134 \cos^2 \theta)
\end{array}
\right\} \quad (166)
$$

where the potentials used in the ^1P state were:

$$
\left.
\begin{array}{lll}
\text{I.} & V(^1P) = -3V(^1S) = +35.7 \text{ Mev} \\[4pt]
\text{II.} & V(^1P) = \ -V(^1S) = +11.9 \text{ Mev} \\[4pt]
\text{III.} & V(^1P) = \ \ \ V(^1S) = -11.9 \text{ Mev}
\end{array}
\right\} \quad (167)
$$

Note that the difference between a repulsive force (I and II) and an attractive force III is shown by the sign of the term in $\cos \theta$ in equation 166, which represents interference between the ^1P and the ^1S states.

The total cross section can be obtained by adding the triplet and the singlet scattering in a 3-to-1 ratio. The three theories give in fractions of a barn the values shown in Table 10.

The total cross section should not be used by itself to make a definite decision between the three theories since it is influenced

TABLE 10

THEORETICAL NEUTRON-PROTON SCATTERING AT 15.3 MEV

Theory	Total Cross Section	Angular Distribution
I	0.621 barn	$1 - 0.080 \cos \theta + 0.077 \cos^2 \theta$
II	0.666 barn	$1 + 0.126 \cos \theta + 0.042 \cos^2 \theta$
III	0.933 barn	$1 + 0.932 \cos \theta + 0.457 \cos^2 \theta$

by the range and the shape chosen for the interaction potential. On the other hand, the angular distribution is good evidence for the existence or non-existence of strong P-scattering, and also gives the sign of that scattering—thus providing direct information about the exchange nature of the neutron-proton force.

For comparison with experiment, we may note from Table 10 that at 15.3 Mev, theory I gives a weak backward maximum, theory II a weak forward maximum, and theory III a strong forward maximum.

EXPERIMENTS ON NEUTRON-PROTON SCATTERING

Total cross sections can be obtained by measuring the absorption of neutrons in paraffin and correcting for the presence of carbon. Angular distributions have been measured by Amaldi and others (Naturwissenschaften **30**, 582, 1942; also Ricerca scientifica 1942), using the recoil protons projected from a paraffin foil. The proton directions are determined by the use of a coincidence-counter "telescope." Proton ranges, hence energies, are determined by the simultaneous use of absorbing foils.

In the center-of-mass system, conservation of momentum requires that the neutron and proton leave each other in opposite directions—i.e., at angles θ and $180° - \theta$ to the incident neutron, respectively. In the laboratory system, the two particles leave at right angles to each other, and the angle between proton and incident neutron is $90° - \theta/2$.

Amaldi found that the number of protons projected forward was small, corresponding to weak neutron scattering in the backward direction, $\theta = 180°$. This is in agreement with ordinary forces III and in contradiction to exchange and symmetric theories II and I. Amaldi measured $R = \sigma(180°)/\sigma(90°)$, the angles being the neutron scattering in the center-of-mass system. His results are given in Table 11 together with their quoted accuracy.

TABLE 11

HIGH-ENERGY NEUTRON-PROTON SCATTERING (AMALDI)

E (in Mev)	$R = \sigma(180°)/\sigma(90°)$
12.5	0.71 ± 0.04
13.3	0.53 ± 0.03
14.0	0.52 ± 0.03

The values of R at 15.3 Mev computed from the cross-section formulas in Table 10 give for the three theories:

$$\text{I. } R = 1.157 \qquad \text{II. } R = 0.916 \qquad \text{III. } R = 0.525 \qquad (168)$$

On the other hand, Champion and Powell (extension of experiments reported in Proc. Roy. Soc. **183**, 64, 1944), using neutrons of similar energy and using photographic techniques, find that the scattering is practically isotropic. However, their experimental data have less good statistics and greater correction factors than Amaldi's.*

More definite evidence contradicting Amaldi's results comes from measurements of the proton-proton scattering at energies of 14.5 Mev by R. R. Wilson and collaborators (Phys. Rev. 1947). Although these experiments are preliminary, they indicate a slight repulsion in the P-state. They might be reconcilable with exchange forces or with zero forces in the P-state, but they appear to fit best to a force of the $\sigma_1 \cdot \sigma_2$ type and they certainly contradict an ordinary force such as would be required by Amaldi's experiments. There is, of course, the logical possibility that neutron-proton and proton-proton scattering are different, but in any case the present state of this subject is inconclusive and more accurate measurements are urgently needed.

* Laughlin and Kruger (Phys. Rev. **71**, 736, 1947) also find isotropic distribution (at 12–13 Mev).—*Note added in proof.*

If Amaldi's results are correct they imply that the forces in the
P-state are attractive, and they support the theory of ordinary
forces III.   Unfortunately, this result cannot be easily reconciled
with the saturation property of nuclear forces.*

* Experiments carried out with the 184-inch cyclotron of the University of
California at the end of 1946 demonstrate definitely the exchange nature of
the forces between neutron and proton.   It was shown in these experiments
that a neutron of about 100 Mev will produce protons mostly in the forward
direction and with energies nearly equal to 100 Mev.   This had been predicted
by Wick for high energy collisions between neutrons and protons.   If the
forces were ordinary forces the proton would in general receive an energy
of the order of the depth of the nuclear potential well, i.e., about 10 Mev.   On
the other hand, if the interaction is of the exchange type, then neutron and
proton will change roles: the neutron will retain an energy of the order of
10 Mev and the proton will take almost the entire energy.   When this note
was written it had not been established whether the forces are of the pure
exchange type or of the type corresponding to the symmetrical meson theory.—
Note added in proof.

XV. SKETCH OF THE MESON THEORY
OF NUCLEAR FORCES

This theory is presented although it has so far not given any results in quantitative agreement with empirical facts on nuclear forces. However, it may give a valuable point of view.

The Coulomb force between two charged particles can be explained in terms of the interaction of these particles with the electromagnetic field. Similarly, the force acting between two nucleons might be described by a meson field surrounding the first particle which acts on the second.

Moving charges produce a radiation field which can be quantized and described in terms of photons. The "quanta" surrounding a nuclear particle are called mesons. Yukawa, in initiating the meson theory (Proc. Physico-Math. Soc. Japan **17,** 48, 1935), suggested that if the mesons are given a finite rest mass m, the range of forces arising from the meson field will be $\hbar/mc$, the Compton wave length for the meson. If the range of nuclear forces is assumed to be 2.8×10^{-13} cm, the meson rest mass should be about 140 electron masses. Particles with about this rest mass were discovered in cosmic rays two years later. In the meantime, Brode and Fretter have determined the rest mass to be 202 ± 10 electron masses, giving a range of 2×10^{-13} cm.

To determine the nature of the meson field and the corresponding nuclear forces, an equation analogous to $\nabla^2 \psi = -4\pi\rho$ must be written for the static part of the electromagnetic field. A relativistic equation suited for particles with no spin and a finite rest mass m is the Klein-Gordon equation:

$$\nabla^2 \psi + (1/\hbar^2 c^2)[(E - V)^2 - (mc^2)^2]\psi = 4\pi\rho \qquad (169)$$

with

$$E = i\hbar(\partial/\partial t) \qquad (169a)$$

where ρ in this case is proportional to the density of nucleons. In free space, $V = 0$. For a *static* meson field, according to equation 169a, we must put $E = 0$. Furthermore, if there is one point-nucleon at the origin, the Klein-Gordon equation becomes

$$\nabla^2 \psi - (mc/\hbar)^2 \psi = 4\pi g_1 \delta(\mathbf{r}) \qquad (170)$$

where δ represents the Dirac δ-function, and g_1 is a constant replacing the electronic charge in electrodynamics.

The solution of this equation is

$$\psi = -(g_1/r) \exp\left[-(mc/\hbar)r\right] \tag{171}$$

and the potential acting on a second nucleon is given by:

$$V = g_2\psi \tag{172}$$

where g_1 and g_2 are the effective nucleonic "charges" or coupling constants.

The Yukawa scalar meson theory just described produces the required range for nuclear forces. Since in this theory the nuclear particle does not change its nature (i.e., charge) we find that according to the theory the neutron-neutron, neutron-proton and proton-proton forces are all equal. However, the theory does not explain the spin-dependence of nuclear forces. Furthermore, the forces are all "ordinary," whereas exchange forces were found to be necessary to explain the saturation of nuclear forces.

Since the mesons discovered in cosmic rays were all charged either positively or negatively, a theory of charged mesons was developed. According to this theory, the following reactions can take place:

$$P \rightleftarrows N + \mu^+ \quad \text{or} \quad N \rightleftarrows P + \mu^- \tag{173}$$

Thus protons and neutrons can transform into each other by the emission or absorption of positive or negative mesons. The interaction between two particles, 1 and 2, can take place, for instance, by the following scheme:

$$P_1 \rightarrow N_1 + \mu^+ \qquad N_2 + \mu^+ \rightarrow P_2 \tag{174}$$

It is clear that such an interaction can only occur between a proton and a neutron, not between two like particles. This is in contradiction to experimental evidence and rules out the charged meson theory, at least in the case of weak coupling between nucleons and meson field (small value of g). Further, the charges of particles 1 and 2 are exchanged in the process of emission and reabsorption of the meson; therefore, this meson theory leads to a force of the charge exchange or Heisenberg type. This, while giving saturation, is in contradiction with experiment (Chapter XIV).

To explain the neutron-neutron and proton-proton forces which are missing in the charged theory, a symmetric scalar meson theory was developed, containing neutral, positive and negative mesons described by three functions ψ_1, ψ_2, and ψ_3. To get spin-dependent nuclear forces, the meson field must further depend on the spin of the nucleon which generates the field. This is achieved by introducing into the Hamiltonian of nucleon plus meson field, an interaction energy containing the factor $\boldsymbol{\sigma} \cdot \text{grad } \psi$ where $\boldsymbol{\sigma}$ is the nucleon spin. In this case ψ must be a "pseudoscalar" since $\boldsymbol{\sigma}$ is an axial and grad a polar vector. (A pseudoscalar changes sign when the sign of the time is reversed, or on inversion of the spatial coordinates; under Lorentz transformations, it is invariant.)

Solution of the symmetric pseudoscalar meson field equation led to an interaction energy between two nucleons of the form

$$V = g^2 \frac{1}{3} \boldsymbol{\tau}_1 \cdot \boldsymbol{\tau}_2 \left[S_{12} \left(\frac{3}{r^3} + \frac{3\mu}{r^2} + \frac{\mu^2}{r} \right) e^{-\mu r} + \boldsymbol{\sigma}_1 \cdot \boldsymbol{\sigma}_2 \frac{\mu^2}{r} e^{-\mu r} \right] \quad (175)$$

where $\mu = mc/\hbar$.

The term in $\boldsymbol{\sigma}_1 \cdot \boldsymbol{\sigma}_2$ provides the spin dependence of nuclear forces, and the tensor force S_{12} explains the existence and sign of the quadrupole moment. All these features are in qualitative agreement with experiment, as shown in the preceding chapters. Unfortunately, the high singularity of V at $r = 0$ makes it impossible to solve the Schrödinger equation.

Two ways of saving the situation have been suggested: (1) to cut off the interaction at some finite radius r_0, i.e., to give the neutrons and the protons a finite size, or (2) to mix two meson theories in such a way as to eliminate the undesirable singularity.

The assumption of finite sources (1) unfortunately cannot be formulated in a relativistic invariant way. Furthermore, use of the rigorous relativistic interaction between nucleon and meson field leads to the reappearance of terms in $1/r^2$ and $1/r^3$ in the "mixed" theories, in higher approximations. Therefore there are at present no trustworthy results of the meson theory of nuclear forces.

It should be noted that many of the statements made about the spin and charge dependence of the nuclear forces have to be modified if the coupling between nucleon and meson field is strong, i.e., if many mesons are emitted simultaneously. The coupling constant for an electromagnetic field is $e^2/\hbar c = \frac{1}{137}$, a small value, whereas that for the meson field $g^2/\hbar c \simeq \frac{1}{4}$ or $\frac{1}{3}$ is considerably larger. The divergence of the interaction at small distances makes the interaction effectively even stronger. For this reason, much effort has been spent to treat the strong coupling problem in meson theory, but so far no results have been obtained which throw light on the problem of nuclear forces.

C. TOPICS NOT RELATED TO NUCLEAR FORCES

XVI. BETA DISINTEGRATION

In Chapter VI, experimental evidence was given for the hypothesis of the production of neutrinos of rest mass 0 and spin $\frac{1}{2}$ in β-decay processes. This assumption made possible the conservation of energy and spin. The first detailed theory of the process was given by Fermi (Zeitschrift für Physik **88**, 161, 1934). A modification which seemed necessary but was later abandoned was the work of Konopinski and Uhlenbeck (Phys. Rev. **48**, 7, 1935). A summary is given by Konopinski (Rev. Modern Phys. **15**, 209, 1943).

Fermi introduced a new interaction between the nucleon and the two light particles, electron and neutrino. His interaction was chosen in analogy with the interaction between charges and electromagnetic field in quantum electrodynamics. (This analogy was also used in the last chapter in connection with the meson theory of nuclear forces.) The heavy particles are to act as sources and sinks of the light particles.

If the Hamiltonian of the interaction between the proton, neutron, and electron-neutrino fields is H, then the number of transition processes per unit time is

$$(2\pi/\hbar)\left|\int \psi_{\text{fin.}}^* H\psi_{\text{in.}}\, d\tau\right|^2 \cdot \rho(E) \qquad (176)$$

where $\rho(E)$ = the number of final states of the system per unit energy interval

$\psi_{\text{in.}}$ = initial state of the system
$\quad = u_{\text{in.}}$ = initial state of the nucleon.

$\psi_{\text{fin.}} = u_{\text{fin.}} \cdot \psi_{\text{elec.}} \cdot \varphi_{\text{n.}}$ = final state of the system
$\quad$ = (final state of nucleon) $\cdot$ (final state of electron)
$\quad \cdot$ (final state of neutrino).

Fermi's assumption for H was essentially

$$\int \psi_{\text{fin.}}^* H\psi_{\text{in.}}\, d\tau = g\int u_{\text{fin.}}^* \psi_{\text{elec.}}^* \varphi_{\text{n.}} u_{\text{in.}}\, d\tau \qquad (177)$$

(neglecting relativistic corrections which are important only if the *heavy* particle has high velocity) where $\psi_{\text{elec.}}$ and $\varphi_{\text{n.}}$ are to be evaluated at the position of the nucleon, and therefore the integral is over the coordinates of the nucleon alone. This is similar to the case of electrons and light: a charge can only interact with a light quantum when they are at the same place. The constant g which determines the strength of the interaction must be found from experiment. It has the dimensions erg · cm³, since $\psi_{\text{elec.}}$ and $\varphi_{\text{n.}}$ are to be normalized per unit volume.

Note that we use $\psi_{\text{elec.}}^*$, but $\varphi_{\text{n.}}$ (without a star). This corresponds to the emission of an electron but the absorption of a neutrino. However, this absorbed neutrino can be taken from a state of negative energy which corresponds to the emission of an "antineutrino." Owing to the absence of charge and magnetic moment, an antineutrino is equivalent to a neutrino. The formulation (177) is therefore equivalent to the emission of an electron and a neutrino, and it is a mathematical convenience to have formally one particle absorbed and one created. The positron emission would be described by $\psi_{\text{elec.}}\varphi_{\text{n.}}^*$.

Since the neutrino has very little interaction with anything, its wave function may be taken as a plane wave. If $\mathbf{p}_{\text{n.}}$ is the momentum of the emitted antineutrino, then $-\mathbf{p}_{\text{n.}}$ is that of the absorbed neutrino of negative energy, and

$$\varphi_{\text{n.}} = V^{-\frac{1}{2}} \exp\left(-i\, \mathbf{p}_{\text{n.}} \cdot \mathbf{r}/\hbar\right) \tag{178}$$

where V is the volume of a box in which the wave function is normalized. The factor $V^{-\frac{1}{2}}$ may be omitted if a unit volume is used for the normalization. $\psi_{\text{elec.}}$ should be a Coulomb wave function; but if Z the charge number is small, the Coulomb energy of the electron can be neglected in comparison with its kinetic energy and a plane wave can be used for the electron wave function. The number of final states per unit energy is

$$\rho(E) = \frac{\text{(Volume element of momentum space of electron)} \times \text{(Volume element of momentum space of neutrino)}}{\text{(Volume of phase space per electron energy state)} \times \text{(Volume of phase space per neutrino energy state)} \times dE}$$

$$= (p_{\text{elec.}}^2\, dp_{\text{elec.}}\, d\omega_{\text{elec.}})(p_{\text{n.}}^2\, dp_{\text{n.}}\, d\omega_{\text{n.}})/(2\pi\hbar)^6\, dE_{\text{n.}} \tag{179}$$

where $d\omega_{\text{elec.}}d\omega_{\text{n.}}$ are elements of solid angle.

The result for the transition probability of an electron into $dE_{\text{elec.}}$ and solid angle $d\Omega/4\pi$ (integration over all directions of the neutrino has been carried out) is

$$\frac{G^2}{2\pi^3}\frac{mc^2}{\hbar}\left|\int u_{\text{fin.}}^* u_{\text{in.}} \exp\left[-i(\mathbf{p}_{\text{n.}}+\mathbf{p}_{\text{elec.}})\cdot\frac{\mathbf{r}}{\hbar}\right]d\tau\right|^2 \epsilon(\epsilon^2-1)^{\frac12}(\epsilon_0-\epsilon)^2\, d\epsilon\,\frac{d\Omega}{4\pi}$$

(180)

with $G = (g/mc^2)(\hbar/mc)^{-3}$, $\epsilon = E_{\text{elec.}}/mc^2$, $\sqrt{\epsilon^2 - 1} = p_{\text{elec.}}/mc$, $\epsilon_0 = E_{\text{available}}/mc^2$. A plane wave has been substituted for the electron wave function.

Just as in the theory of atomic transitions, there will be selection rules for β-decay processes. If $p_{\text{elec.}}$ and $p_{\text{n.}}$ are both of the order of magnitude mc, as is usually the case, the exponent $(\mathbf{p}_{\text{n.}} + \mathbf{p}_{\text{elec.}})$ $\cdot\, \mathbf{r}/\hbar$ will be of the order of magnitude:

$$\frac{R}{\hbar/mc} \approx \frac{4 \times 10^{-13} \text{ cm}}{3.86 \times 10^{-11} \text{ cm}} \sim \frac{1}{100} \tag{181}$$

(R = nuclear radius; medium-weight nuclei have been chosen.) Thus, $\exp[i(\mathbf{p}_{\text{n.}} + \mathbf{p}_{\text{elec.}}) \cdot \mathbf{r}/\hbar]$ will be nearly 1, and the matrix element in equation 180 reduces to $M = \int u_{\text{fin.}}^* u_{\text{in.}}\, d\tau$, i.e., to an expression depending only on the state of the nucleon before and after the transition. M is determined by the nuclear wave functions. In particular, the orthogonality of the nuclear wave functions for states of different angular momentum I gives the selection rule:

$$M \neq 0 \text{ implies } \Delta I = 0 \tag{182}$$

Such transitions are called allowed. Transitions for which $M = 0$ are called forbidden; in this case the exponential in equation 180 must be expanded in a power series; the order of the forbidden transition is the number of the first term in this power series which gives a non-vanishing result for the matrix element. Because of the estimate (181), the probabilities should decrease by a factor of about 10^4 with each order.

ALLOWED TRANSITIONS

The only dependence of the allowed transition probability on the electron energy is through the volume element in momentum space. The energy spectrum of electrons is therefore

$$N(\epsilon)\, d\epsilon \sim \epsilon\sqrt{\epsilon^2 - 1}(\epsilon_0 - \epsilon)^2\, d\epsilon \tag{183}$$

Since ϵ_0 is unknown, the experiments have to yield a value of ϵ_0, while giving a check on the theoretical spectrum. This is easily done by making a "Kurie plot." In this plot, the quantity

$$F(\epsilon) = \sqrt{N(\epsilon)/\epsilon(\epsilon^2 - 1)^{\frac{1}{2}}} \qquad (184)$$

(as observed) is plotted against the energy ϵ. According to equation 183, $F(\epsilon) \sim \epsilon_0 - \epsilon$; therefore the plot should yield a straight line which cuts the ϵ-axis at ϵ_0.

The only nucleus which checks this proportionality exactly is In^{114}, measured by Lawson and Cork (Phys. Rev. **57**, 982, 1940).

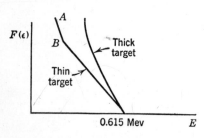

FIG. 13. Kurie plot of the positron spectrum from Cu^{64}.

Here $\epsilon_0 = 1.99$ Mev (which is high enough to make the experiments on the β-rays fairly easy) and the lifetime is 72 seconds. Luckily this short-lifetime β-decay follows a 50-day-lifetime γ-decay (isomeric transition; see Chapter IV).

There are experimental difficulties in the measurement of the energy spectra of most other β-radioactive nuclei which result from either the low energy of the electrons or the short lifetimes. Cu^{64} measured by A. W. Tyler (Phys. Rev. **56**, 125, 1939) emits both positrons and electrons. The positron spectrum was measured both for thick target and thin target (thick and thin relative to the electron range). The Kurie plots are shown in Fig. 13. It is not known whether the portion AB of the thin target curve is spurious or results from another decay process (to an excited state of Ni^{64}) with a very low energy limit.

The thick target curve is typical of the experimental evidence which lead Konopinski and Uhlenbeck to introduce their alternative theory (Phys. Rev. **48**, 7, 1935). They proposed using the time derivative of the neutrino wave function $\partial\varphi/\partial t$ in the transition probability instead of φ. Since $\partial\varphi/\partial t \sim (\epsilon_0 - \epsilon)\varphi$ this led to spectrum

$$N_{\text{K-U}} \, d\epsilon \sim \epsilon\sqrt{\epsilon^2 - 1}(\epsilon_0 - \epsilon)^4 \, d\epsilon \qquad (185)$$

thereby moving the maximum of the spectrum to lower electron energies. To make a Kurie plot of this, the fourth root must be used in equation 184 instead of the second. Many of the experimental data on thick targets then give straight lines but very high values of ϵ_0. Later experiments using thin targets showed that the Kurie plots according to the Konopinski-Uhlenbeck theory dropped off, as shown in Fig. 14, which demonstrated that the straight-line portion was accidental. Also, when the mass differences of nuclei became better known, the values of ϵ_0 given by the Konopinski-Uhlenbeck theory were shown to be much too high in all cases but that those given by the Fermi theory agreed with the measured mass difference.

N^{13} measured by Kikuchi et al. (Proc. Physico-Math. Soc. Japan, **21**, 52, 1939); Lyman (Phys. Rev. **55**, 1123, 1939); and

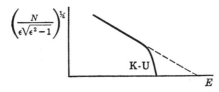

FIG. 14. Typical Kurie plot of the Konopinski-Uhlenbeck theory.

Townsend (Proc. Roy. Soc. **A177**, 357, 1941), is one case in which the use of very thin targets still did not give a Fermi distribution. To account for such spectra it is usually assumed that several decay processes are taking place simultaneously, leading to various energy levels of the residual nucleus. With $N^{13} \rightarrow C^{13} + \beta^+$ this is confirmed by the observation of a γ-ray of about 280 kev by Richardson (Phys. Rev. **55**, 609, 1939). This γ-ray is attributed to the transition of the residual nucleus C^{13} from its excited to the ground state. Unfortunately, various experimenters disagree on the relative intensities of the γ-rays and of the two components of the β-spectrum, and on the value of the upper limit of its lower-energy component.

Coulomb Field. In expression 183 for the electron energy spectrum no account has been taken of the Coulomb field. The correct spectrum has a greater electron density at low energies. There is no zero for $\epsilon = 1$ because the factor $\sqrt{\epsilon^2 - 1} \sim v$ (velocity) in the density of states is canceled by a $1/v$ in the charge density of electrons at the nucleus.   The resulting electron spectrum is shown in Fig. 15.

For positrons, fewer of low energy should be expected than the number given by expression 183 because of the repulsion of the positrons in the Coulomb field: The Coulomb wave function of the electron in expression 177 has a factor exp $(-2\pi Ze^2/\hbar v)$, which lowers the transition probability considerably for low velocities.

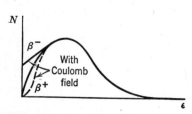

FIG. 15.   Energy distribution of β-rays with Coulomb field.

There are some disturbing measurements by Backus (Phys. Rev. **68**, 59, 1945) on the ratio of positrons to electrons, N_+/N_-, in the Cu^{64} β-transitions:

$$Cu^{64} \rightarrow \begin{cases} Ni^{64} + \beta^+ \\ Zn^{64} + \beta^- \end{cases}$$

N_+/N_- should be smallest and behave in a calculable way at low energies; the experimental values were compared with the theoretical prediction but the value of N_+/N_- was found to be ten times greater than predicted.   These measurements should be repeated.   The disagreement can hardly be attributed to a failure of β-ray theory because the ratio of positron emission to K-electron capture was found to be in exact agreement with theory (Scherrer et al., Phys. Rev. **68**, 57, 1945), and this ratio involves parts of the theory very similar to those in Backus' experiment.

LIFETIMES IN ALLOWED TRANSITIONS

The total transition probability, or reciprocal of the lifetime, for β-ray emission is found by integrating over the energy distribution (equation 180) to be

$$1/\tau = (G^2/2\pi^3) \cdot (mc^2/\hbar)|M|^2 F(\epsilon_0) \qquad (186)$$

G is a dimensionless constant describing the strength of the inter-action between electron-neutrino and the heavy particles. M is the matrix element for the transition:

$$M = \int u_{fin.}*(\mathbf{r})u_{in.}(\mathbf{r})e^{-i(\mathbf{p_n.}+\mathbf{p}_e)\cdot\mathbf{r}/\hbar}\,d\tau \qquad (187)$$

$F(\epsilon_0)$ is the integral of the distribution in energy

$$F(\epsilon_0) = \int_1^{\epsilon_0} \epsilon \sqrt{\epsilon^2 - 1} (\epsilon_0 - \epsilon)^2 \, d\epsilon \tag{188}$$

where ϵ_0 is the total energy available for neutrino and electron, including rest mass, in units of the electron rest energy. $F(\epsilon_0)$ varies rapidly with ϵ_0, being approximately equal to $(1/30)\epsilon_0{}^5$ for $\epsilon_0 \gg 1$ and to $0.216(\epsilon_0 - 1)^{7/2}$ for ϵ_0 nearly unity. Thus τ decreases rapidly with increasing ϵ_0, but not as fast as in the case of α-decay, where the transition probability is proportional to an exponential of the energy. In Chapter II it was pointed out that in natural α-decay a factor of 2 in energy is equivalent to a factor of 10^{-20} in lifetime.

The matrix element M is in general not known because we have very scant knowledge of nuclear wave functions. Even if we know that the transition is allowed, we can in general say only that $|M|$ is between zero and one.

However, in some cases the value of M can be guessed to somewhat better than order of magnitude. For allowed transitions $(\Delta I = 0)$, we have

$$M \approx \int u_{\text{fin.}}{}^* u_{\text{in.}} \, d\tau \tag{189}$$

M will be near unity when the wave functions $u_{\text{fin.}}$ and $u_{\text{in.}}$ are nearly alike. Such is the case for β-transition between mirror nuclei (Chapter II) (for which also the selection rule $\Delta I = 0$ is likely to be fulfilled). Three examples of allowed transitions in mirror nuclei are given in Table 12. The product $tF(\epsilon_0)$ is remark-

TABLE 12

ALLOWED TRANSITIONS IN MIRROR NUCLEI

Reaction	t = half-life	ϵ_0	$tF(\epsilon_0)$
$H^3 \rightarrow He^3 + \beta^- + \nu$	10^9 sec	1.03	1400
$C^{11} \rightarrow B^{11} + \beta^+ + \nu$	1200 sec	2.86	3500
$Sc^{41} \rightarrow Ca^{41} + \beta^+ + \nu$	0.9 sec	10.68	2500

Source: Konopinski, Rev. Modern Phys. **15**, 209.

ably constant, confirming the theory underlying equation 186. This constancy exists in spite of t varying by a factor as large as 10^9. Furthermore, it is reasonable that tF is somewhat smaller for the first situation than for the other two, for in a nucleus containing only three particles we would expect $u_{\text{fin.}}$ and $u_{\text{in.}}$ to be more nearly alike than in the heavier nuclei, so that $|M|$ would be closer to unity in the light nucleus.

It is interesting to note that the Konopinski-Uhlenbeck theory of β-decay predicts variation by a factor of 10^5 between the products tF for the various reactions in Table 12.

For nuclei of intermediate mass, the Coulomb repulsion already introduces considerable asymmetry between the numbers of pro-

TABLE 13

ALLOWED TRANSITIONS IN INTERMEDIATELY HEAVY NUCLEI

Reaction	$tF(\epsilon_0)$
$S^{35} \rightarrow Cl^{35} + \beta^- + \nu$	19,000
$Cu^{64} \rightarrow Zn^{64} + \beta^- + \nu$	66,000
$Cu^{64} \rightarrow Ni^{64} + \beta^+ + \nu$	22,000
$In^{117} \rightarrow Sn^{117} + \beta^- + \nu$	140,000

tons and neutrons (there are no more mirror nuclei), and presumably even greater differences between neutron and proton wave functions in the nucleus. Thus, even for allowed transitions, smaller matrix elements are expected for intermediately heavy nuclei than for light, mirror nuclei. This is borne out by the data in Table 13.

In the heavy, naturally radioactive nuclei the matrix elements

TABLE 14

ALLOWED TRANSITIONS IN NATURALLY RADIOACTIVE NUCLEI

Emitter	$tF(\epsilon_0)$
RaB	50,000
UX$_2$	270,000

are in general still smaller. This is borne out by the data in Table 14.

Assuming $|M| \approx 1$ for the lightest mirror nuclei, G can be calculated from Ft. The result is

$$G \approx 10^{-11} \tag{190}$$

This corresponds to $g \approx 10^{-48}$ erg $\cdot$ cm^3. The smallness of this coupling between electron-neutrino and the heavy particle is what makes β-decay take place so slowly compared to other nuclear reactions, except some α-radiation. It is safe to say that *β-rays are not emitted during nuclear collisions*, but only at comparatively long times afterwards. For example, the lifetime of protons in the sun due to the reaction

$$H + H \rightarrow D + \beta^+ + \nu \tag{191}$$

is about 10^{11} years, even with a density of about 100 and a temperature of 2×10^7 degrees C. (See Bethe and Critchfield, Phys. Rev. **54**, 248.) Even so, this reaction presents about the best opportunity for β-decay during a collision. The long lifetime of the proton in the sun indicates an extremely low probability of β-decay per collision.

The most fundamental β-decay is that of the neutron

$$n \rightarrow H + \beta^- + \nu \tag{192}$$

The matrix element for this reaction should be exactly unity, as the wave function for a single proton ought to be the same as that of a single neutron. Measuring the lifetime of this reaction should give an exact value of G. However, this reaction is hard to observe as the neutrons are removed much more rapidly by other means (capture, diffusion) than by the above reaction. Using the value of G found above, the half-life for the reaction (192) should be about 15 minutes. There is hope of making the measurement with the large neutron fluxes now available in piles.

LIFETIMES IN FORBIDDEN TRANSITIONS

The second term in the Taylor expansion of the exponential in the matrix element (187) will give a non-vanishing integral when $\Delta I = \pm 1$, which transition was forbidden in the first approximation. Similarly, $\Delta I = \pm 2$ transitions become possible with the third term in the expansion, and so on. For $\epsilon_0 = 2$, the argument of the exponential averages about $1/100$ over the range of the heavy particle wave function, so that $|M(\Delta I = \pm 1)|^2$ might be expected to be about 10^{-4} times $|M(\Delta I = 0)|^2$. Actually, the true wave function for an electron in the Coulomb field varies faster than the plane wave approximation used in equation 187, and the factor 10^{-4} becomes about 10^{-2} for medium and heavy nuclei. This correction does not help the higher forbidden transitions so much as the first. Higher ϵ_0 makes all forbidden transitions more probable. Table 15 quotes experimental data from Konopinski for forbidden transitions in light nuclei.

TABLE 15

HALF-LIVES IN FORBIDDEN TRANSITIONS

Emitter	t = Half-life	ϵ_0	$tF(\epsilon_0)$
First Forbidden Transitions			
Li^3	0.9 sec	24.5	2.8×10^5
Ne^{23}	40 sec	9	10^5
Second Forbidden Transitions			
P^{32}	1.2×10^6 sec	4.37	8.6×10^7
Higher Forbidden Transitions			
Be^{10}	10^{14} sec	2.1	10^{14}
K^{40}	5.10^{16} sec	2.4	10^{17}

Source: Konopinski, Rev. Modern Phys. **15**, 209.

GAMOW-TELLER SELECTION RULES

There is good evidence that the selection rule $\Delta I = 0$ for allowed transitions is not generally adhered to. One example is the K-capture reaction

$$Be^7 + K \to Li^7 + \nu \qquad (193)$$

Li^7 is produced both in its ground state and in an excited state about 440 kev above the ground state. The experimental ratio of number of transitions to the ground state to number of transitions to the excited state is about 10 to 1. This is about equal to the calculated ratio, using equation 186 and assuming $|M|$ equal for the two cases. From this and the absolute lifetime it may be concluded that both transitions are allowed. However, we do not expect both states of Li^7 to have the same value for I. The best assumption is that the two states form a P-doublet, with $I = \frac{1}{2}$ and $I = \frac{3}{2}$ for excited and ground states, respectively. Thus ΔI can certainly not be zero for both transitions.

Another example is the reaction:

$$He^6 \to Li^6 + \beta^- + \nu \qquad (194)$$

Li^6 can be thought of as an α-particle plus a deuteron. The α-particle has $I = 0$, and the deuteron has $I = 1$. We expect, therefore, that Li^6 has $I = 1$, in agreement with experiment. In the same picture, He^6 is an α-particle plus two neutrons. In the "ground state," the double neutron should have spin zero (cf. Chapter XII), so that the same argument gives $I = 0$ for He^6. An additional argument for this is that all nuclei containing even numbers of neutrons and protons have zero spin as far as they have been investigated. Thus $\Delta I = 1$, and the transition is forbidden. But the experimental lifetime of the reaction shows that it is "allowed." There are similar situations in the β-decay of C^{10}, F^{18}, and Na^{22}.

So it seems that there can be allowed transitions with $\Delta I = 1$.

Gamow and Teller first showed how this can come about. They said that in considering possible interactions, one ought to include all relativistically invariant combinations of the four wave functions, $u_{in.}$, $u_{fin.}$, $\psi_{elec.}$, and $\phi_{n.}$. For *two* wave functions, let us say ψ and ϕ, there are five combinations which are covariant under Lorentz transformations:

1. Scalar: $\psi^* \beta \phi$ (Fermi theory).
2. Polar four vector, with components: $\psi^* \phi$, $\psi^* \mathbf{a} \phi$.
3. Tensor: $\psi^* \beta \boldsymbol{\sigma} \phi$, $\psi^* \beta \mathbf{a} \phi$.
4. Axial vector: $\psi^* \boldsymbol{\sigma} \phi$, $\psi^* \gamma_5 \phi$.
5. Pseudoscalar: $\psi^* \beta \gamma_5 \phi$.

where β, $\mathbf{a}$, and γ_5 are Dirac operators and $\boldsymbol{\sigma}$ is the usual spin operator. (For details, see Konopinski's article.) To obtain a relativistically invariant interaction, the corresponding combinations of the wave functions of the light and of the heavy particles must be multiplied; for example, the tensor combination of the light particle wave functions with the tensor combination of the wave functions $u_{in.}$ and $u_{fin.}$ of the heavy particles. In this case the Hamiltonian becomes:

$$V(\text{tensor}) = (\psi^* \beta \sigma \phi) \cdot (u_{fin.}^* \beta \sigma u_{in.}) \qquad (195)$$

(The transition is still treated as though an antineutrino is emitted.) Since the heavy particles are non-relativistic, the Dirac operator β for them is equivalent to unity; therefore, the net effect of equation 195 is to place the operator σ between the heavy particle wave functions $u_{in.}$ and $u_{fin.}$. Therefore, the matrix element for allowed transitions is now $\int u_{fin.}^* \sigma u_{in.} \, d\tau$, and this may be different from zero if the total spin I changes by one unit, or by zero, in the transition. Thus $\Delta I = \pm 1, 0$ can be "allowed" for the tensor interaction.

The axial vector interaction gives the same selection rule as the tensor,

$$\Delta I = 0, \pm 1 \tag{196}$$

From the experimental data it seems that these Gamow-Teller selection rules are correct. For instance, they explain the results for He^6, C^{10}, F^{18}, and Na^{22}. However, the reaction

$$Be^{10} \rightarrow B^{10} + \beta^- + \nu \tag{197}$$

differs from (194) only by the addition of an α-particle, so that $\Delta I = 1$ may again be expected for this reaction. But experiment shows that this is forbidden. The same is true for the reaction

$$C^{14} \rightarrow N^{14} + \beta^- + \nu \tag{198}$$

which differs from (194) by two α-particles. Thus the Gamow-Teller selection rules, while explaining more than the Fermi rules, still are in contradiction with many of the data.

K-capture. The theory for *K*-capture has been worked out, and is in good agreement with experiment. Scherrer et al. (Phys. Rev. **68**, 57) have measured the ratio of *K*-capture processes to positron-emission processes for Cd^{107} (or ^{109}?), with the result: 320 ± 20. The Fermi theory predicts 340. (The Konopinski-Uhlenbeck theory gives 20,000, and is conclusively ruled out.)

XVII. THE COMPOUND NUCLEUS

In this chapter, we are no longer concerned with the determination of fundamental nuclear forces, but with the more practical problem of predicting cross sections for nuclear reactions, particularly those involving heavier nuclei the quantum states of which are not known precisely. On the other hand, the presence of many nuclear particles will make statistical methods practical, and these are used in the theory of the compound nucleus.

The concept of the compound nucleus was initiated by Bohr in 1935. In order to get a clear picture of this concept we shall examine the difference between nuclear collisions and atomic collisions.

For collisions between an atom and a particle of high or moderate energy, the Born approximation is valid because the incident particle passes right through the atom practically undisturbed. Slight deflections, inelastic collisions, and emission of radiation are progressively less likely processes. The reason that particles are likely to pass right through is that the atom is a loosely bound structure. Another way of saying this is that the interaction of atomic electrons with, say an incident electron of several thousand volts, is much smaller than the incident energy—which is precisely the condition for validity of Born's approximation.

Nuclear interactions, on the other hand, are of the order of 20 Mev, which is much greater than the kinetic energy of the incident particle normally used, i.e., several Mev or less. This is precisely the opposite of the conditions required for Born's approximation. Here, the interaction energy is more important than the kinetic energy.

Another difference: An electron striking an atom can be regarded as interacting with the average "Hartree" field of the atom. This approximation is valid because the interaction with a single electron is much smaller than the average interaction with all the electrons. On the other hand, the short range and the saturation character of nuclear forces require that nucleons interact only with a small number of neighbors. Thus individual interactions will be of the same order of importance as the average total inter-action—and it will not be permissible to replace the nucleus by an average field.

The Bohr picture takes advantage of these large interactions and describes them in terms of a compound nucleus. The theory makes the following statements:

1. *Any particle which hits the nucleus is caught.* A new nucleus is formed called the *compound nucleus.* The reason for this is that an incident particle will interact with one or two nucleons, transferring much of its energy to them and thus to the nucleus, before penetrating it appreciably. Then it may no longer have sufficient kinetic energy to escape the attractive nuclear forces, and is therefore caught.

2. The *compound nucleus is long-lived* compared to the natural nuclear time. (This is the time for a neutron to cross the nucleus— say 10^{-12} cm$/10^9 \frac{\text{cm}}{\text{sec}} \simeq 10^{-21}$ second.) The reason for this is that the compound nucleus, which is in an excited state (excitation energy above the ground state = incident energy + binding energy of one particle), will live until this excitation energy, or a reasonable fraction of it, is concentrated again on *one* particle.

3. The final *break-up* of the nucleus is *independent of the mode of formation,* i.e., regardless of how the nucleus was formed there will be definite probabilities for decay into each of several possible residual nuclei. This can be explained in terms of the long life-time of the compound nucleus during which complete statistical equilibrium is assumed to be established—thus the nucleus forgets how it was formed; formation and disintegration can be regarded as independent events.

For example, the ordinary Al nucleus ($^{13}\text{Al}^{27}$) can be formed as a "compound nucleus" in a highly excited state from any of the reactions:

$$\left.\begin{array}{l} ^{11}\text{Na}^{23} + {}^2\text{He}^4 \rightarrow {}^{13}\text{Al}^{27} \text{ excited} \\[4pt] ^{12}\text{Mg}^{25} + {}^1\text{H}^2 \ \rightarrow {}^{13}\text{Al}^{27} \text{ excited} \\[4pt] ^{12}\text{Mg}^{26} + \ \text{H}^1 \ \rightarrow {}^{13}\text{Al}^{27} \text{ excited} \\[4pt] ^{13}\text{Al}^{27} + \ \ \gamma \ \ \ \rightarrow {}^{13}\text{Al}^{27} \text{ excited} \end{array}\right\} \tag{199}$$

The compound nucleus can then decay back, reversing the reac-tion, into any of the nuclei just mentioned, or also into $\text{Al}^{26} + n$, with a definite probability for each which is the same for all modes of formation. The residual nuclei may also be left in excited states, with probabilities which are also independent of the manner of formation.

Formation of Compound Nucleus. The cross section for formation of the compound nucleus σ_f may be written in the form

$$\sigma_f = \pi R^2 \xi \qquad (200)$$

where R is the nuclear radius, and ξ is a useful parameter, called the sticking probability, which is defined by this equation.

For fast nuclear particles, i.e., $\lambda \ll R(\lambda \sim 10^{-12}$ cm for 200-kv neutrons), the classical geometrical approach is valid since the uncertainty in position of the particle is only λ. The cross section for capture of fast nuclear particles is certainly not greater than πR^2 since the interaction is negligible if the particle passes at a distance from the nucleus. For slow neutrons, however, cross sections greater than πR^2 are possible since the position of the particle is poorly defined. To get a sticking probability which is always ≤ 1, the definition is revised. We define the *contribution* σ_l to the cross section due to particles of orbital momentum l, and set

$$\sigma_l = (2l + 1)\pi\lambda^2\xi_l \qquad (201)$$

Then from general principles of quantum mechanics, ξ_l must be less than (or equal to) 1. Moreover, equation 201 reduces to equation 200 for high energy since all values of l up to R/λ will contribute appreciably (cf. Chapter IX, p. 38); ξ is a weighted average of ξ_l. Neutrons were used in the above discussion to avoid questions involving penetration of the potential barrier which would arise for protons and α-particles.

The Bohr statement, that any particle which hits the nucleus is caught, is given more precisely by the equation

$$\xi \to 1 \text{ as } \lambda/R \to 0 \qquad (202)$$

In other words, the sticking probability approaches 1 at high energies. This statement has been checked experimentally with high-energy neutrons especially by Amaldi and co-workers, by Sherr, and by Graham and Seaborg. They find cross sections of about $\sigma_f \simeq \pi R^2$, with R given by a formula similar to equation 3, in good agreement with other methods of determining nuclear radii (see Chapter II).

Disintegration of Compound Nucleus.   The probability that the compound nucleus will disintegrate in a particular way is related to the cross section for the corresponding inverse capture process with some factors containing the density of initial and final states. This follows from considering a statistical equilibrium condition between the compound nucleus and all the possible states of all the residual nuclei into which it can disintegrate (similar to Chapter XI, p. 60).   In equilibrium, the number of nuclei present in a small energy range between E and $E + dE$ will be proportional to the density of states $\rho(E)$ in that energy range, and to a Boltzmann factor.   Since energy is conserved in the total system, the Boltzmann factors cancel out and the condition for equilibrium takes the form

$$\rho_A W_{A \to B} = \rho_B W_{B \to A} \qquad (203)$$

where ρ_A and ρ_B are the densities of initial and final states of the system at corresponding energies, and the W's represent probabilities for the direct and inverse processes.

For our process, A is the excited compound nucleus with a density of states $\rho_A(E_A) = 1/D_A$, where D is the average separation between neighboring states, at an energy E_A above the ground state of A.   (Each state is counted according to its statistical weight.) $W_{A \to B}$ is the probability of disintegration of the compound nucleus into a *definite* state of the residual nucleus B with energy E_B above its ground state, with the emission of a particle (say neutron) of energy E. $W_{B \to A}$ is the probability that nucleus B will capture this particle of energy E and produce a compound state of excitation E_A.   Finally, $\rho_B(E_B)$ gives the number of states between E and $E + dE$ available for the outgoing particle, viz.

$$\rho_B = \frac{4\pi p^2}{v(2\pi\hbar)^3} \qquad (203a)$$

with p and v the momentum and velocity of the outgoing particle. We now use the relation between the capture probability and the capture cross section, which is

$$W_{B \to A} = v\sigma_f(E) \qquad (204)$$

for one neutron in a box of unit volume moving with velocity $v = (2E/m)^{\frac{1}{2}}$, and the relation between the excitation energies E_A and E_B,

$$E_B = E_A - E - B \qquad (205)$$

where E is the energy of the outgoing particle and B its binding energy in the unexcited nucleus A.

Using all the relations just given, and setting $l = 0$ in equation 201 (other l give very similar results), we now have a relation by means of which the disintegration probability $W_{A \to B} \equiv \Gamma_B/\hbar$ can be computed in terms of the sticking probability ξ_B for the inverse capture reaction:

$$(1/D_A)(\Gamma_B/\hbar) = \rho_B v \,\pi \lambdabar^2 \xi_B \tag{206}$$

or, inserting 203a and simplifying:

$$\Gamma_B/D_A = \xi_B/2\pi \tag{206a}$$

This important equation relates the disintegration probability Γ_B, leading to a definite state of the residual nucleus, to the level spacing D_A. For high energies, ξ_B approaches 1; for low energies it is proportional to the velocity v of the emitted particle. Both D_A and Γ_B can be deduced from experiment; D_A and ξ_B can also be estimated from various statistical models for heavy nuclei (Nuclear Physics B; Weisskopf, Phys. Rev. **52,** 295, 1937; **57,** 472, 1940).

The disintegration probabilities $\Gamma_B/\hbar$ are also related to the widths of the resonances observed in these reactions: since the total decay probability is

$$\Gamma/\hbar = (1/\hbar)\sum_B \Gamma_B \tag{207}$$

the time dependence of the wave function is of the form

$$e^{-iEt/\hbar}e^{-\Gamma t/2\hbar} = e^{-i(E - \frac{1}{2}i\Gamma)t/\hbar} \tag{208}$$

(Note that the absolute *square* of the wave function gives the occupation of the state and decays according to equation 207.) Equation 208 has a Fourier transform * the absolute square of which is:

$$\frac{1}{(E' - E)^2 + (\Gamma/2)^2} \tag{209}$$

Thus Γ has the same dimensions as E and gives the width at half-maximum of the level, or resonance line. The quantity Γ_B repre-

---

* Taking the Fourier transform with respect to time of a time-dependent wave function gives the wave function $\psi(E')$ in energy space.

sents a *partial level width*, i.e., the contribution to Γ arising from the disintegration into a definite end state B.

Since the compound nucleus must eventually decay, the cross section for a reaction ending in state B is given by the cross section for forming the compound nucleus, times Γ_B/Γ. Thus

$$\sigma_{fB} = \sigma_f \, \Gamma_B/\Gamma \qquad (210)$$

and for fast particles:

$$\sigma_{fB} = \pi R^2 \xi \, \Gamma_B/\Gamma \qquad (211)$$

CONCLUSIONS ABOUT NUCLEAR REACTIONS

Energy Distribution of Emitted Particles. From equation 206a we see that Γ_B is almost the same for any final state B, since the sticking probability ξ_B is a slowly varying function of the energy of the outgoing particle. This information is useful in predicting the energy distribution of the emitted particles. For example, if we consider the inelastic scattering of neutrons

$$Z^A + n \rightarrow Z^{A+1} \rightarrow Z^A + n \qquad (212)$$

and make use of the fact that the density of states in the *residual* nucleus increases rapidly with excitation energy, then we see that the residual nucleus will most likely be left in a fairly high excited state and the emitted neutron will come out with low energies.

The fact that emitted neutrons come out with greatly reduced energies has been experimentally confirmed for many target nuclei. Lead forms a notable exception to this rule. The reason for this may be that the first excited state in this instance is quite high— so that this rule would not be confirmed unless higher energy incident neutrons are used. In fact, the incident energy must be high enough so that the residual nucleus B possesses a great many levels with an excitation energy less than the incident kinetic energy E_0, in order that the statistical considerations used may be valid.

Shadow Scattering. In neutron-scattering experiments a purely wave-optical effect must be considered at high incident energies ($\lambda \ll R$), for which we have said the capture cross section is πR^2. In this case, the nucleus can be regarded as a black sphere of radius R which casts a shadow. This is described in the language of wave optics by saying that just enough light is scattered in the forward direction to cancel the incident beam. This would mean a cross section for shadow scattering of πR^2. Furthermore, to cancel the incident beam behind the sphere, this shadow scattering must be of the same energy, i.e., it represents elastic scattering. According to an elementary wave-optical argument, the shadow scattering will be mostly confined to an angle λ/R from the forward direction.

In the case of light, for which normally $\lambda \ll R$, the shadow scattering is not easily measurable since the shadow extends practically to infinity. In the nuclear case λ/R is, say, $\frac{1}{3}$ or $\frac{1}{5}$, so that the umbra or region of complete shadow extends only a short distance back of the nucleus, certainly not as far back as the measuring apparatus. Thus it is possible to make measurements outside the main beam but still at small enough angles to it to obtain the elastic shadow scattering. The existence and general features of shadow scattering have been confirmed experimentally by Kikuchi et al., Amaldi et al., and Bacher.

Charged Particles. The emission of charged particles such as protons requires the penetration of a potential barrier. This penetration probability is similar to that given in the theory of α-decay and is quite small unless the emitted protons have energy nearly equal to, or greater than, the barrier height B. Thus, in a rough way, we may say that the protons must leave with a minimum energy B. This would leave the residual nucleus at a lower energy than if neutrons were emitted. Since the density of residual nucleus states decreases rapidly with decreasing energy, the probability for proton emission will be much smaller than that for neutron emission because of the fewer number of states available, especially if the nuclear charge is high and the available energy low.

γ-rays. The emission of γ-rays will in general be small compared to heavy particle emission when the latter is energetically possible because the coupling of the nucleus with the radiation field involves the small factor $c^2/\hbar c = 1/137$.

DENSITY OF NUCLEAR ENERGY LEVELS—
NUCLEAR TEMPERATURE

The density of nuclear energy levels increases rapidly as a function of energy. To see how this comes about a model which is only a crude approximation is used. We consider the nuclear particles as independent of each other, and suppose each of them has a set of equally spaced energy levels spaced by an energy difference Δ. Then, the excited states of the system will also be spaced by the interval Δ, and will have a greater statistical weight the greater the excitation energy, because of the greater number of ways of dividing the energy among the particles. When an interaction among the particles is then introduced, there will be splitting of each energy level; and the statistical weight of an energy level of the non-interacting system is a measure of the energy level density in the same region of the spectrum, after the interaction has been introduced.

To calculate the level density a model of the nucleus must be used. Four models will be mentioned. (For more details see Nuclear Physics B, p. 79.)

1. *Free Particles in a Box of the Size of the Nucleus.* The level spacing D is proportional to $\exp(-\sqrt{E})$, where E is the excitation energy of the nucleus. For $A = 120$, $E = 8$ Mev, we get $D \sim 10$ ev, which is about what is observed.

2. *Free Particle in a Box, with Correlations.* Bardeen has pointed out that the free particle model must be modified to be in accord with the assumption of exchange forces. The result gives a level spacing depending on excitation energy in about the same way as before, but the level spacings are somewhat wider: $D \sim 100$ ev for $A = 120$, $E = 8$ Mev.

3. *Lattice Model.* This model is the opposite extreme of models 1 and 2, for the particles are here supposed to be firmly bound and capable only of small vibrations about equilibrium. The results are similar to those for models 1 and 2. The level spacing is proportional to $\exp(-E^{4/7})$. For $A = 120$ and $E = 8$ Mev, $D \sim 100$ ev.

4. *Liquid Drop Model.* For heavy nuclei this model is quite a good approximation. The level spacing is proportional to $\exp(-E^{4/7})$ for small E and $\exp(-E^{3/4})$ for larger E. For $A = 120$ and $E = 8$ Mev, $D \sim 10$ ev.

All these models give a level spacing which is a decreasing function of the energy of the form $\exp[-f(E)]$, where $f(E)$ is a slowly variable function of the energy.

If the density of states, $\rho(E) = 1/D$, of *any* system is given as a function of energy then an entropy can be defined as

$S = k \log \rho(E)$, and a temperature as $\partial S/\partial E = 1/T(E)$. Each of the four models mentioned will therefore define a nuclear temperature as a function of excitation energy. It turns out that for 10 Mev excitation energy, kT is of the order of 1 Mev, i.e., $T = 10^{10°}$ K.

The most satisfactory treatment of nuclear thermodynamics (Weisskopf, Phys. Rev. **52**, 295, 1937) avoids a model and supposes

$$D = C \exp(-B\sqrt{E}) \tag{213}$$

The constants B and C are determined from experiment: For low excitation energies the exponential is close to 1 so that D is about equal to C. From the observed position of the lowest excited levels, it is found that:

For light nuclei $(A \sim 20)$ $C \sim 10^6$

For heavy nuclei $(A \sim 200)$ $C \sim 10^5$ $\tag{214}$

B can then be determined from neutron resonance levels near $E \sim 8$ Mev (binding energy of neutron in nucleus); this gives about:

$B = 2$ for light nuclei

$B = 4$ for heavy nuclei $\tag{215}$

if E is measured in Mev.

Any of the level density functions lead approximately to a Boltzmann distribution for inelastically scattered neutrons. If the incident energy of the neutrons is E_0 and the energy of the emitted neutrons is W then the excitation energy of the residual nucleus is $E_0 - W$. Supposing that the level density of the residual nucleus is $\exp[+f(E)]$ and expanding,

$$f(E) = f(E_0) - f'(E_0)W + \cdots \tag{216}$$

we get a level density

$$\exp f(E) = \exp f(E_0) \times \exp(-f'W) \tag{217}$$

Therefore, setting $f' = 1/kT$ (which is exactly the expression demanded by $\partial S/\partial E = 1/T$) gives a Boltzmann distribution for the level density of the residual nucleus as a function of W and therefore for the kinetic energies of the emitted neutrons. A more careful consideration gives a probability of emission proportional to $\sqrt{W}\,\exp(-W/kT)$ or $W\,\exp(-W/kT)$ but experiment has not as yet given enough data to make it possible to distinguish between them.

RESONANCE PHENOMENA

Let the energy levels of a nucleus Z^A be as shown in Fig. 16 and consider the process $Z^{A-1} + n \to Z^A$. If the incident neutron has exactly the right energy to form Z^A in one of its excited states, the probability of capture is large. Such energies are called resonance energies of the compound nucleus. The experimental

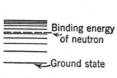

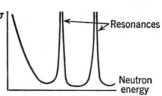

| Fig. 16.   Energy levels of a nucleus. | Fig. 17.   Typical experimental cross section of a nucleus for slow neutrons. |

evidence (see Fig. 17) for neutron resonance energies in capture processes led to the first theories of the compound nucleus. Experimentally, for $A \sim 100$, the level spacing D is about 10 ev, if E is about the binding energy of the neutron, i.e., 8 Mev. D is about the same at $A \sim 200$, and the appropriate binding energy $E \sim 5$ Mev. This can be understood because, on the one hand, the number of particles is greater (and thus there are more possibilities of distributing the energy); on the other hand the excitation energy (binding energy of the particle) is smaller. For A smaller than 100, the level spacing increases rapidly.

There are several nuclei for which more than one resonance is known: Among elements having only one (abundant) isotope, In has 3 resolved resonances, I has 5, and Ta 7. In addition, many other elements show more resonances than isotopes. Most of the experimental evidence was obtained by Rainwater, Havens, and their collaborators, in several papers in Phys. Rev. **71** (1947). In some cases, only one resonance is observed; the level spacing is then not directly known but it can be taken as of the same order of magnitude as the kinetic energy of the neutrons corresponding to the first resonance.

For *protons*, capture resonances have been observed only for the very light nuclei. The level spacings are of the order of 10 to 100 kev with an excitation energy of ~10 Mev. For heavier nuclei, the Coulomb barrier prevents capture resonances for protons because the excitation energies which result after a proton has been given sufficient energy to get over the Coulomb barrier are so high that the resonance levels overlap. A few resonances have also been observed for α-particles, the reactions of which lead mostly to the emission of protons or neutrons.

The width Γ of a nuclear energy level is defined as $\Gamma \equiv \hbar/\tau$, where τ is the lifetime of the level. For most of the slow neutron capture levels the width is about 0.1 ev. This can be decomposed

$$\Gamma = \Gamma_\gamma + \Gamma_n \qquad (218)$$

into the neutron width and the γ-ray width. Almost all of Γ is Γ_γ, which means that capture is far more probable than scattering for slow neutron resonances.* Γ_n may be determined separately in two different ways. First, the capture cross section at exact resonance is given by

$$(\text{const}) \times \Gamma_n/E_r\Gamma \qquad (219)$$

Γ is the width of the resonance at half-maximum; therefore, Γ_n can be determined from σ at resonance, Γ and E_r. Second, the ratio of scattering to capture cross sections at resonance is Γ_n/Γ_γ, and Γ_γ is very nearly equal to Γ. Unfortunately, in order to get the scattering cross section at resonance it must be disentangled from the potential scattering (Nuclear Physics B, p. 152) so that this second method is ordinarily not of much use.

The first experiments on neutron capture were done by Fermi and his collaborators, and by Moon and Tillman, using an ingenious but rather complicated method: a neutron beam from which the thermal neutrons had been removed by a cadmium absorber impinged on an indium detector. Comparison of the radioactivities produced in this detector with and without an indium absorber intervening, showed that neutrons which activated the indium detector were strongly captured by the indium absorber. If a silver absorber was used instead, the absorption was small. On

---

* Mn has a strong resonance at about 300 ev which gives mostly scattering and therefore has $\Gamma_n \gg \Gamma_\gamma$. This is to be expected for light nuclei because of their large level spacing; see equation 206a.—*Note added in proof.*

the other hand, a silver detector showed about as much radio-activity with and without the indium absorber, but with a silver absorber the beam was very strongly attenuated. The conclusion was that indium and silver were activated by neutrons of two different energies. At present, the most satisfactory method consists in using a modulated cyclotron beam and determining the velocity of the neutrons by their time of flight to the target. For very slow neutrons, a pile and a crystal spectrometer are often preferable.

THE DISPERSION FORMULA

Breit and Wigner were the first to develop a theory of nuclear resonance processes. The result was analogous to that in the theory of optical dispersion

$$\sigma \sim \frac{1}{(E - E_r)^2 + (\Gamma/2)^2} \tag{220}$$

The measurements using velocity selection can check the shape of this curve and at the same time determine E_r and Γ. To get the coefficient of proportionality in equation 220, suppose that the cross section σ is for the production of B with A incident. Then, since the cross section is proportional to the half-width for disintegration into B, it must contain Γ_B. It also must contain Γ_A for symmetry reasons. This follows from the principle of detailed balance: apart from statistical weights and a factor depending on the ratios of momenta, $\sigma_{A \to B}$ should be equal to $\sigma_{B \to A}$. (See Chapter XI.)

Finally we know that for the simplest case in which only one kind of particle can be emitted or absorbed, $\Gamma_A = \Gamma_B = \Gamma$, and we know further that in this instance the largest possible cross section for particles with $l = 0$ is $4\pi\lambda^2$. Clearly, in the general case, the wave length of the incident particle must occur. Collecting all information,

$$\sigma = \pi\lambda_A{}^2 \frac{\Gamma_A \Gamma_B}{(E - E_r)^2 + (\Gamma/2)^2} \tag{221}$$

This is known as the one-level Breit-Wigner formula. It gives the correct dependence on momentum, in accord with the principle of detailed balance

$$\sigma_{B \to A}/\sigma_{A \to B} = \lambda_B{}^2/\lambda_A{}^2 = p_A{}^2/p_B{}^2 \tag{222}$$

For the dependence on the spin of the compound nucleus and the generalization to more than one resonance level see Nuclear Physics B, p. 101. There is only one instance in which the many-level formula has been of use, namely,

$$He^4 + n \rightarrow He^5 \rightarrow He^4 + n \qquad (223)$$

which has two partly overlapping resonances near 1 Mev.

The dispersion formula has been derived many times. The derivation must be quite different from the treatment in optics, where the interaction of the incident light and the atom can be taken as a small perturbation.

For high-energy neutrons the dispersion theory goes over into the statistical theory given previously. The partial widths of the levels become of the order of magnitude of the level spacing and the resonances are no longer observable.

For extremely slow neutrons, well below the first resonance, Γ_A is proportional to v (this follows from the fact that Γ_A is proportional to the density of states in momentum space, $p^2(dp/dE) \sim p$) and so the Breit-Wigner formula reduces to

$$\sigma \sim \lambdabar^2 v \sim 1/v \qquad (224)$$

This is the well-known $1/v$ law for the cross section at very low energy. It makes the number of processes per second, which is σv, independent of the energy distribution and proportional only to the total particle density. For very light nuclei, the spacing D is very large and the $1/v$ law holds up considerable energies. For $B^{10} + n \rightarrow B^{11}$ it is valid to 50,000 ev. Absorption by B^{10} is therefore used for measuring neutron velocities.

APPENDIX: TABLE OF NUCLEAR SPECIES

Column 1: "Z." Atomic number of the element.

Column 2: "Element." Chemical symbol of element.

Column 3: "A." Mass number of the isotope.

Column 4: "Abund., per cent." Per cent abundance of isotope in the naturally occurring element.

Column 5: "Disintegration." Symbols for nuclear processes are:

I Isomeric transition. (Emission of γ-rays or conversion electrons.)

K Electron capture.

e^- Internal conversion electrons.

β^-, β^+ Negative, positive beta-particle emission.

α Alpha-particle emission.

n, H Emission of neutrons, protons.

U Denotes that the particular isotope has not been identified with complete certainty. Parentheses enclosing one or more activities denote uncertainty in these, but not in the identification of the isotope to which they are assigned. Thus, $^{47}Ag^{108}$ has been classified and found definitely to have β^- activity; however, it is not certain that $^{47}Ag^{108}$ also has K-capture and conversion electrons. A comma setting off Ie^- from one or more symbols indicates that the conversion electrons belong to the isomeric transition.

Columns 6 and 7: Masses, with probable errors. A value in parentheses indicates that the mass has been estimated from theory, the isotope not having been produced as yet.

Column 8: Spin of the designated isotope.

MAIN REFERENCES

G. T. Seaborg, Table of Isotopes, Rev. Modern Phys. **16**, 1, 1944.

E. Segre, Isotope Chart, issued by Los Alamos Scientific Laboratory, 1946.

In general, isotopes classified as A to D by Seaborg and Segre have been included in this table, i.e., all those for which at least the assignment to a definite element is certain.

Z	Element	A	Abund., per cent	Disinte- gration	Mass	Error × 10⁵	Spin
0	n	1			1.008 93	3	½
1	H	1	99.98		1.008 123	0.6	½
		2	0.02		2.014 708	1.1	1
		3		β^-	3.017 02	3.4	½
2	He	3	$\sim 10^{-5}$		3.017 00	4	
		4	100		4.003 90	3	0
		5		n	5.013 7	35	
		6		β^-	6.020 9	50	
3	Li	5		H	(5.013 6)	60	
		6	7.5		6.016 97	5	1
		7	92.5		7.018 22	6	³⁄₂
		8		β^-	8.025 02	7	
4	Be	6			(6.021 9)	100	
		7		K	7.019 16	7	
		8		α	8.007 85	7	
		9	100		9.015 03	6	³⁄₂
		10		β^-	10.016 77	8	
		11			(11.027 7)		
5	B	9			9.016 20	7	
		10	18.4		10.016 18	9	1
		11	81.6		11.012 84	8	³⁄₂
		12		β^-	12.019 0	70	
		13			(13.020 7)		
6	C	10		β^+	10.021 0	30	
		11		β^+	11.014 95	9	
		12	98.9		12.003 82	4	0
		13	1.1		13.007 51	10	½
		14		β^-	14.007 67	5	
		15			(15.016 5)		
7	N	12			(12.023 3)		
		13		β^+	13.009 88	7	
		14	99.62		14.007 51	4	1
		15	0.38		15.004 89	21	½
		16		β^-	>16.006 5 <16.011		
		17			(17.014)		
8	O	14			(14.013 1)		
		15		β^+	15.007 8	40	
		16	99.757		16.000 000	Standard	0
		17	0.039		17.004 50	6	
		18	0.204		18.004 9	40	
		19		β^-	19.013 9		

Z	Element	A	Abund., per cent	Disinte-gration	Mass	Error × 10⁵	Spin
9	F	16			(16.017 5)		
		17		β^+	17.007 5	30	
		18		β^+	18.006 5	60	
		19	100		19.004 50	26	½
		20		β^-	>20.004 2		
					<20.009 2		
		21			(21.005 9)		
10	Ne	18			(18.011 4)		
		19		β^+	19.007 81	20	
		20	90.00		19.998 77	10	0
		21	0.27		20.999 63	22	
		22	9.73		21.998 44	36	0
		23		β^-	23.001 3		
11	Na	21		β^+	21.003 5		
		22		β^+	21.999 9	50	
		23	100		22.996 18	31	3⁄2
		24		β^-	23.997 5	45	
		25		$U \beta^-$	(24.996 7)		
12	Mg	22			(22.006 2)		
		23		β^+	23.000 2	40	
		24	77.4		23.992 5	60	0
		25	11.5		24.993 8	90	
		26	11.1		25.989 8	50	
		27		β^-	26.992 8	150	
13	Al	25		β^+	24.998 1	100	
		26		β^+	25.992 9	150	
		27	100		26.989 9	80	5⁄2
		28		β^-	27.990 3	70	
		29		β^-	28.989 3	80	
		30			(29.995 4)		
14	Si	27		β^+	26.994 9	90	
		28	89.6		27.986 6	60	
		29	6.2		28.986 6	70	
		30	4.2		29.983 2	90	
		31		β^-	30.986 2	60	
		32			(31.984 9)		
15	P	29		β^+	28.991 9	100	
		30		β^+	29.987 3	10	
		31	100		30.984 3	50	½
		32		β^-	31.982 7	40	
		33			(32.982 6)		
		34		β^-	33.982 6	40	

Z	Element	A	Abund., per cent	Disinte-gration	Mass	Error × 10^5	Spin
16	S	31		β^+	30.989 9		
		32	95.1		31.980 89	7	0
		33	0.74		32.980 0	60	
		34	4.2		33.977 10	33	
		35		β^-	34.978 8	80	
		36	0.016		35.978	100	
		37		β^-	36.982 1	30	
17	Cl	33		β^+	32.986 0		
		34		β^+	33.980 1	200	
		35	75.4		34.978 67	21	5/2
		36		$\beta^+ \beta^- K$	35.978 8	100	
		37	24.6		36.977 50	14	5/2
		38		β^-	37.981	300	
		39			(38.979 4)		
18	A	35		β^+	34.985 0		
		36	0.307		35.978 0	100	
		37		K	36.977 7		
		38	0.061		37.974	250	
		39			(38.975 5)		
		40	99.632		39.975 6	60	
		41		β^-	40.977 0	60	
19	K	37			(36.983 0)		
		38		β^+	37.979 5		
		39	93.38		38.974 7		3/2
		40	0.012	$\beta^- K$	39.976 0	100	4
		41	6.61		40.974		3/2
		42		β^-			
		43		$U \beta^-$			
20	Ca	39		$U \beta^+$			
		40	96.96		39.975 3	150	0
		41		$U K e^-$			
		42	0.64		41.971 1		
		43	0.15		42.972 3		
		44	2.06				
		45		β^-			
		46	0.0033				
		48	0.19				
		49		β^-			
21	Sc	41		β^+			
		43		β^+			
		44		$I e^-$			
		45	100		44.966 9	60	7/2
		46		$\beta^- K$			

Z	Element	A	Abund., per cent	Disinte-gration	Mass	Error × 10⁵	Spin
21	Sc	47		$U \beta^-$			
(*cont.*)		48		β^-			
		49		β^-			
22	Ti	45		β^+			
		46	7.95		45.966 1	100	
		47	7.75		46.964 7	100	
		48	73.45		47.963 1	50	
		49	5.51		48.964 6	60	
		50	5.34		49.962 1	40	
		51		β^-	50.958 7	100	
23	V	47		$U \beta^+$			
		48		$\beta^+ K$			
		49		$U K$			
		50		β^+			
		51	100		50.957 7	50	½
		52		β^-			
24	Cr	49		β^+			
		50	4.49				
		51		$U K e^-$	50.958		
		52	83.78		51.956		
		53	9.43		52.956		
		54	2.30				
		55		U			
25	Mn	51		β^+			
		52		$\beta^+ K$			
		54		K			
		55	100		54.957		⅝
		56		β^-			
26	Fe	53		β^+			
		54	6.04		53.957		
		55		$K e^-$			
		56	91.57		55.956 8	170	
		57	2.11		56.957		
		58	0.28				
		59		β^-			
27	Co	55		β^+			
		56		$\beta^+ K$			
		57		$\beta^+ K e^-$			
		58		$\beta^+ K$			
		59	100				½
		60		$\beta^-, I e^-$			

Z	Element	A	Abund., per cent	Disinte-gration	Mass	Error $\times 10^5$	Spin
28	Ni	57		β^+			
		58	67.4		57.959 4	40	
		59		$U\ \beta^+$			
		60	26.7		59.949 5	40	
		61	1.2		60.953 7	150	
		62	3.8		61.949 3	40	
		63		β^-			
		64	0.88		63.947 1	60	
29	Cu	58		β^+			
		60		β^+			
		61		$\beta^+\ K$			
		62		β^+			
		63	70.13		62.957	400	$\frac{3}{2}$
		64		$\beta^-\ \beta^+\ K$			
		65	29.87		64.955	400	$\frac{3}{2}$
		66		β^-			
30	Zn	63		β^+			
		64	50.9		63.955	400	0
		65		$\beta^+\ K\ e^-$			
		66	27.3		65.954	400	
		67	3.9		66.954	400	$\frac{5}{2}$
		68	17.4		67.955	300	
		69		$\beta^-\ I$			
		70	0.5		69.954	300	
31	Ga	64		$U\ \beta^+$			
		65		$K\ e^-$			
		66		β^+			
		67		$K\ e^-$			
		68		β^+			
		69	61.2		68.952	800	$\frac{3}{2}$
		70		β^-			
		71	38.8		70.952	900	$\frac{3}{2}$
		72		β^-			
		74		$U\ \beta^-$			
32	Ge	69		U			
		70	21.2				
		71		$\beta^+\ K\ e^-$			
		72	27.3				
		73	7.9				
		74	37.1				
		75		β^-			
		76	6.5				
		77		β^-			
		78		$U\ \beta^-$			

Z	Element	A	Abund., per cent	Disintegration	Mass	Error $\times 10^5$	Spin
33	As	72		$U\ \beta^+$			
		73		$U\ \beta^+\ K\ e^-$			
		74		$\beta^-\ \beta^+$			
		75	100				$\frac{3}{2}$
		76		$\beta^-\ \beta^+\ K$			
		77		$U\ \beta^-$			
		78		β^-			
34	Se	74	0.9				
		75		$K\ e^-$			
		76	9.5				
		77	8.3				$\frac{1}{2}$
		78	24.0				
		79		$U\ \beta^-,\ I\ e^-$			
		80	48.0				0
		82	9.3				
		83		β^-			
35	Br	78		$\beta^+\ e^-$			
		79	50.6				$\frac{3}{2}$
		80		$\beta^-,\ I\ e^-$			
		81	49.4				$\frac{3}{2}$
		82		β^-			
		83		β^-			
		84		β^-			
		85		β^-			
		87		$U\ \beta^-$			
36	Kr	78	0.35				
		79		$U\ \beta^+$			
		80	2.01				
		81		$U\ I\ e^-$			
		82	11.53				
		83	11.53	$I\ e^-$			$\frac{9}{2}$
		84	57.11				
		85		β^-			
		86	17.47				
		87		$U\ \beta^-$			
		88		β^-			
		89		β^-			
		90		$U\ \beta^-$			
		91		$U\ \beta^-$			
		92		$U\ \beta^-$			
		94		$U\ \beta^-$			
		95		$U\ \beta^-$			

Z	Element	A	Abund., per cent	Disintegration	Mass	Error $\times 10^5$	Spin
37	Rb	82		U			
		84		U			
		85	72.8				$\frac{5}{2}$
		86		β^-			
		87	27.2	β^-			$\frac{3}{2}$
		88		β^-			
		89		β^-			
		90		$U\,\beta^-$			
		91		$U\,\beta^-$			
		92		$U\,\beta^-$			
		94		$U\,\beta^-$			
		95		$U\,\beta^-$			
38	Sr	84	0.56				
		85		$I\,e^-\,K$			
		86	9.86				
		87	7.02	$I\,e^-$			$\frac{9}{2}$
		88	82.56				0
		89		β^-			
		90		$U\,\beta^-$			
		91		$U\,\beta^-$			
		92		$U\,\beta^-$			
		94		$U\,\beta^-$			
		95		$U\,\beta^-$			
39	Y	86		$U\,K$			
		87		$(I\,e^-)\,K$			
		88		$\beta^+\,(K)$			
		89	100				
		90		β^-			
		91		$U\,\beta^-,\,I\,e^-$			
		92		$U\,\beta^-$			
		94		$U\,\beta^-$			
		95		$U\,\beta^-$			
40	Zr	89		$\beta^+,\,I$ or $K,\,e^-$			
		90	48.0				
		91	11.5				
		92	22.0				
		93		$U\,\beta^-$			
		94	17.0				
		95		$U\,\beta^-$			
		96	1.5				
		97		$U\,\beta^-$			
41	Cb	90		$U\,\beta^+$			
		91		$U\,K\,e^-$			
		92		β^-			

Z Element		A	Abund., per cent	Disinte-gration	Mass	Error $\times 10^5$	Spin
41	Cb	93	100				9/2
(cont.)		94		β^-			
		95		$U \beta^-, I e^-$			
		96		U			
		97		$U \beta^-$			
42	Mo	92	14.9				
		93		$U \beta^+$			
		94	9.4		93.945	800	
		95	16.1		94.946	800	½
		96	16.6		95.944	800	
		97	9.65		96.945	900	½
		98	24.1		97.943	900	
		99		$U \beta^-$			
		100	9.25				
		101		$U \beta^-$			
		102		$U \beta^-$			
43	Tc	96		$U K$			
		98		$U K e^-$			
		99		$U, I e^-$			
		101		$U \beta^-$			
		102		$U \beta^-$			
44	Ru	96	5.68		95.945	1100	
		98	2.22		97.943	1100	
		99	12.81		98.944	1100	
		100	12.70		99.942	1100	
		101	16.98		100.946	1100	
		102	31.34		101.941	1100	
		103		β^-			
		104	18.27				
		105		β^-			
		106		$U \beta^-$			
		107		$U \beta^-$			
45	Rh	102		$\beta^- \beta^+$			
		103	100	I	102.941	1100	
		104		$\beta^-, I e^-$			
		105		β^-			
		106		$U \beta^-$			
		107		$U \beta^-$			
46	Pd	102	0.8		101.941	1100	
		104	9.3		103.941	1100	
		105	22.6		104.942	900	
		106	27.2		105.941	1000	
		108	26.8		107.941	1000	

Z	Element	A	Abund., per cent	Disinte-gration	Mass	Error $\times 10^5$	Spin
46	Pd	109		$U \beta^-$			
(*cont.*)		110	13.5		109.941	1000	
		111		β^-			
		112		β^-			
47	Ag	105		$U K$			
		106		$\beta^+ K e^-$			
		107	51.9	$(I e^-)$	106.945	600	½
		108		$\beta^- (K e^-)$			
		109	48.1		108.944	700	½
		110		β^-			
		111		β^-			
		112		β^-			
48	Cd	106	1.4				
		107		$U K$			
		108	1.0				
		110	12.8				
		111	13.0				½
		112	24.2				
		113	12.3				½
		114	28.0				
		115		β^-			
		116	7.3				
		117		β^-			
		118		$U, I e^-$			
49	In	110		$U \beta^+$			
		111		$U \beta^+ e^-$			
		112		$U, I e^-, K e^-$			
		113	4.5	$I e^-$			9⁄2
		114		$I e^-, \beta^-$			
		115	95.5	$I e^-$			9⁄2
		116		β^-			
		117		$\beta^- e^-$			
50	Sn	112	1.1				
		113		$K e^-$			
		114	0.8				
		115	0.4		114.940	1400	½
		116	15.5		115.939	1400	
		117	9.1		116.937	1400	½
		118	22.5		117.937	1400	
		119	9.8		118.938	1400	½
		120	28.5		119.937	1400	
		121		$U \beta^-$			
		122	5.5		121.945	1400	
		123		$U \beta^-$			

Z	Element	A	Abund., per cent	Disinte-gration	Mass	Error $\times 10^5$	Spin
50	Sn	124	6.8		123.944	1400	
(cont.)		125		$U\ \beta^-$			
		127		$U\ \beta^-$			
		128		$U\ \beta^-$			
51	Sb	120		β^+			
		121	56				$\frac{5}{2}$
		122		β^-			
		123	44				$\frac{7}{2}$
		124		β^-			
		126		$U\ \beta^-$			
		127		β^-			
		128		$U\ \beta^-$			
		129		β^-			
		132		β^-			
		133		$U\ \beta^-$			
		136		$U\ \beta^-$			
52	Te	120	0.088				
		121		$(K\ e^-)$			
		122	2.43	$(I\ e^-)$			
		123	0.85				
		124	4.59				
		125	6.93				
		126	18.71				
		127		$\beta^-,\ I\ e^-$			
		128	31.86				
		129		$\beta^-,\ I\ e^-$			
		130	34.52				
		131		$\beta^-,\ I\ e^-$			
		132		$U\ \beta^-$			
		133		$U\ \beta^-$			
		135		β^-			
		136		$U\ \beta^-$			
		137		$U\ \beta^-$			
53	I	124		β^+			
		126		$\beta^-\ K$			
		127	100				$\frac{5}{2}$
		128		β^-			
		130		β^-			
		131		β^-			
		132		$U\ \beta^-$			
		133		β^-			
		135		β^-			
		136		$U\ \beta^-$			
		137		$U\ \beta^-$			

Z	Element	A	Abund., per cent	Disintegration	Mass	Error $\times 10^5$	Spin
54	Xe	124	0.094				
		126	0.088				
		127		$U, I\,e^-$			
		128	1.90				
		129	26.23				½
		130	4.07				
		131	21.17				¾
		132	26.96				
		133		$(\beta^-)\,I\,e^-$			
		134	10.54				
		135		$\beta^-\,I$			
		136	8.95				
		137		$U\,\beta^-$			
		138		$U\,\beta^-$			
		139		β^-			
		140		β^-			
		141		β^-			
		143		$U\,\beta^-$			
		144		$U\,\beta^-$			
55	Cs	130		U			
		132		$U\,K\,e^-$			
		133	100				⅞
		134		β^-			
		136		$\beta^-\,K\,e^-$			
		137		$U\,\beta^-$			
		138		$U\,\beta^-$			
		139		β^-			
		140		$U\,\beta^-$			
		141		β^-			
		142		$U\,\beta^-$			
		143		U			
56	Ba	130	0.101				
		132	0.097				
		133		$I\,e^-$			
		134	2.42				
		135	6.59				¾
		136	7.81				0
		137	11.32				¾
		138	71.66				0
		139		β^-			
		140		β^-			
		141		β^-			
		142		$U\,\beta^-$			
		143		$U\,\beta^-$			
		145		$U\,\beta^-$			

Z	Element	A	Abund., per cent	Disinte-gration	Mass	Error $\times 10^5$	Spin
57	La	137		$U\ K$			
		139	100		138.953	800	$\frac{7}{2}$
		140		β^-			
		141		β^-			
		143		$U\ \beta^-$			
		144		$U\ \beta^-$			
		145		$U\ \beta^-$			
58	Ce	136	<1				
		138	<1				
		140	89	(I)			
		141		β^-			
		142	11				
		143		$U\ \beta^-$			
		144		$U\ \beta^-$			
		145		$U\ \beta^-$			
		147		$U\ \beta^-$			
59	Pr	140		β^+			
		141	100				$\frac{5}{2}$
		142		β^-			
		143		$U\ \beta^-$			
		144		$U\ \beta^-$			
		145		$U\ \beta^-$			
		147		$U\ \beta^-$			
60	Nd	141		β^+			
		142	25.95				
		143	13.0				
		144	22.6				
		145	9.2		144.962	400	
		146	16.5		145.962	400	
		148	6.8		147.962	400	
		150	5.95		149.964	400	
61	61	143		$U\ \beta^-$			
		144		$U\ I$ or K			
		145		$U\ \beta^-$			
		146		U			
		147		$U\ \beta^-$			
62	Sm	144	3				
		146		$U\ I$			
		147	16.1				
		148	14.2	α			
		149	15.5				

Z	Element	A	Abund., per cent	Disinte-gration	Mass	Error × 10⁵	Spin
62	Sm	150	11.6				
(cont.)		151		$U\ \beta^-$			
		152	20.7				
		154	18.9				
63	Eu	151	49.1				5/2
		152		$U\ \beta^-\ e^-$			
		153	50.9				5/2
		154		$U\ \beta^-$			
		155		$U\ \beta^-$			
		156		$U\ \beta^-$			
		157		$U\ \beta^-$			
		158		$U\ \beta^-$			
64	Gd	152	0.2				
		154	1.5		153.971	600	
		155	18.4		154.971	600	
		156	19.9		155.972	600	
		157	18.9		156.973	600	
		158	20.9		157.973	600	
		160	20.2		159.974	600	
65	Tb	159	100				3/2
		160		β^-			
66	Dy	158	>0.1				
		160	0.1				
		161	21.1				
		162	26.6				
		163	24.8				
		164	27.3				
		165		β^-			
67	Ho	165	100				7/2
		166		$U\ \beta^-$			
68	Er	162	0.1				
		164	1.5				
		166	32.9				
		167	24.4				
		168	26.9				
		169		$U\ \beta^-$			
		170	14.2				
69	Tm	169	100				1/2
		170		(β^-)			

Z	Element	A	Abund., per cent	Disinte-gration	Mass	Error $\times 10^5$	Spin
70	Yb	168	0.06				
		170	4.21				
		171	14.26				$\frac{1}{2}$
		172	21.49				
		173	17.02				$\frac{5}{2}$
		174	29.58				
		175		U			
		176	13.38				
71	Lu	175	97.5				$\frac{7}{2}$
		176	2.5	$\beta^-\ K$			≥ 7
		177		$U\ \beta^-$			
72	Hf	174	0.18				
		176	5.30				
		177	18.47				$\leq \frac{3}{2}$
		178	27.10				
		179	13.85				$\leq \frac{3}{2}$
		180	35.11				
		181		β^-			
73	Ta	180		$(\beta^-)\ K\ e^-$			
		181	100	I			$\frac{7}{2}$
		182		β^-			
74	W	180	~ 0.2				
		182	22.6				
		183	17.3				$\frac{1}{2}$
		184	30.1				
		185		$U\ \beta^-$			
		186	29.8				
		187		$U\ \beta^-$			
75	Re	184		$U\ K$			
		185	38.2				$\frac{5}{2}$
		186		$U\ \beta^-$			
		187	61.8				$\frac{5}{2}$
		188		$U\ \beta^-$			
76	Os	184	0.018				
		186	1.59				
		187	1.64	K			
		188	13.3				
		189	16.1		189.04	2000	$\frac{1}{2}$ or $\frac{3}{2}$
		190	26.4		190.03	2000	
		191		$U\ \beta^-$			
		192	41.0		192.04	2000	
		193		$U\ \beta^-$			

Z	Element	A	Abund., per cent	Disintegration	Mass	Error $\times 10^5$	Spin
77	Ir	191	38.5		191.04	2000	$\frac{1}{2}$
		192		β^-			
		193	61.5		193.04	2000	$\frac{3}{2}$
		194		β^-			
78	Pt	192	0.8				
		194	30.2		194.039	1400	
		195	35.3		195.039	1400	$\frac{1}{2}$
		196	26.6	$(I\,e^-)$	196.039	1400	
		197		$U\,\beta^-$			
		198	7.2		198.05	2000	
		199		β^-			
79	Au	196		$U\,\beta^-\,e^-$			
		197	100	I	197.04	1000	$\frac{3}{2}$
		198		$\beta^-\,e^-$			
		199		β^-			
		200		$U\,\beta^-$			
80	Hg	196	0.15				
		197		$K\,e^-$			
		198	10.1				0
		199	17.0	$I\,e^-$			$\frac{1}{2}$
		200	23.3				0
		201	13.2				$\frac{3}{2}$
		202	29.6				0
		203		$U\,\beta^-$			
		204	6.7				0
		205		β^-			
81	Tl	198		$U\,K\,e^-$			
		199		$U\,K\,e^-$			
		202		$U\,K\,e^-$			
		203	29.1		203.05	2000	$\frac{1}{2}$
		204		$U\,\beta^-$			
		205	70.9		205.05	2000	$\frac{1}{2}$
		206		$U\,\beta^-$			
	AcC″	207		β^-			
	ThC″	208		β^-			
	Tl	209		β^-			
	RaC″	210		β^-			
82	Pb	203		$U\,\beta^+$			
		204	1.5		204.05	2000	
		205		$U, I\,e^-$			
		206	23.6		206.05	2000	0
		207	22.6		207.05	2000	$\frac{1}{2}$

Z	Element	A	Abund., per cent	Disinte-gration	Mass	Error $\times 10^5$	Spin
82	Pb	208	52.3		208.05	2000	0
(cont.)		209		β^-			
	RaD	210		β^-			
	AcB	211		β^-			
	ThB	212		β^-			
	Pb	213		β^-			
	RaB	214		β^-			
83	Bi	207		$K\ e^-$			
		209	100		209.05	2000	$\frac{9}{2}$
	RaE	210		β^-			
	AcC	211		$\beta^-\ \alpha$			
	ThC	212		$\beta^-\ \alpha$			
	Bi	213		$\beta^-\ \alpha$			
	RaC	214		$\beta^-\ \alpha$			
84	Po	210		α			
	AcC′	211		α			
	ThC′	212		α			
	Po	213		α			
	RaC′	214		α			
	AcA	215		α			
	ThA	216		$\beta^-\alpha$			
	Po	217		α			
	RaA	218		$\beta^-\ \alpha$			
85	At	211		$K\ \alpha$			
86	An	219		α			
	Tn	220		α			
	Rn	221		α			
	Rn	222		α			
87	87(AcK)	223		$U\ \beta^-$			
88	AcX	223		α			
	ThX	224		α			
	Ra	225		α			
	Ra	226		α			
	MsTh$_1$	228		β^-			
89	Ac	227		$\beta^-\ \alpha$			
	MsTh$_2$	228		$\beta^-\ \alpha$			
90	RdAc	227		α			
	RdTh	228		α			
	Th	229		α			
	Io	230		α			
	UY	231		β^-			

Z	Element	A	Abund., per cent	Disinte-gration	Mass	Error $\times 10^5$	Spin
90	Th	232	100	α	232.11	3000	
(*cont.*)	Th	233		β^-			
	UX_1	234		β^-			
91	Pa	231		α			$\frac{3}{2}$
		232		β^-			
		233		$\beta^-\ e^-$			
	UZ	234		β^-			
	UX_2	234		$\beta^-\ I$			
92	U	233		α			
	UII	234	0.00518	α			
	AcU	235	0.719	α			
	U	237		β^-			
	UI	238	99.274	α	238.12	3000	
	U	239		β^-			
93	Np	234		K			
		235		K			
		236		β^-			
		237		α			
		238		β^-			
		239		β^-			
94	Pu	238		α			
		239		α			
95	Am	241		α			
96	Cm	240		α			
		242		α			

· INDEX